Proceedings of the conference held in London   April 1987

# high tech BUILDINGS 87

## online Publications
**London : New York**

H626662g

British Library Cataloguing in Publication Data

```
High-tech buildings '87 : proceedings of
  the conference held in London, April 1987.
  1. Commercial buildings  2. Technological
  innovations
  690'.52      TH4311

  ISBN 0-86353-085-0
```

**Online Publications**
A Division of Online International Ltd,  London : New York

**online**

Online International is the world's leading specialist in the design,
co-ordination and management of conferences and exhibitions concerned
with the business implications and applications of leading-edge
technology.  With a schedule spanning some 20 technology areas, many
Online events have achieved world forum status.  The company was
formed in 1971 and now employs more than 100 specialists based in
London and New York.

Online International Ltd
Pinner Green House, Ash Hill Drive, Pinner, Middlesex HA5 2AE, UK
Phone: 01-868 4466    Telex: 923498 ONLINE G    Fax: 018689933

# Introduction

The opening of the Lloyd's building, Victoria Plaza, Chase Manhattan Bank and other partially integrated high-tech buildings has shown the way forward for the high-tech building industry. A <u>fully</u> integrated communications, computer and energy management system is now a realistic goal.

The papers in this book highlight the technological and financial forces at play within the industry. They also cover the effect of innovations in communications technology and environmental control systems. With contributors ranging from architects to consulting engineers to networks specialists this is essential reading for all concerned with the high-tech building industry and its future.

Online publish a wide range of conference proceedings in closely associated areas of technology. Please turn to page 233 for further information.

iv

# Session Chairmen

John Ellis
Consultant,
J&J Ellis & Associates

Sir Monty Finniston
President, Industrial
Building Bureau

David Firnberg
Managing Director,
Eosys & Chairman
The Networking Centre

Derek Gregory
Director, BSRIA

Derek Thorogood
Head of Building
Engineering Services,
BBC Television

# Contents

* To incorporate the most recent material available, this paper has been included out of sequence.

x

# Authors

# High-tech buildings:
# understanding the segmentation of the market

David Firnberg
Managing Director, Eosys Limited: and
Chairman, The Networking Centre

An important element in understanding the concept of high tech buildings is to understand the segmentation of the market. This paper sets out to answer the following questions:

- What is a high tech building and how does it relate to an intelligent building?

- What are the technological developments affecting this market?

- How important are standards and regulations to the climate for investment in intelligent buildings?

- Does the life cycle of an intelligent building make it an economic proposition?

DAVID FIRNBERG is Managing Director of Eosys, the information technology consultancy. He is also Chairman of The Networking Centre based in Hemel Hempstead which tests products for conformance to the OSI standards, including MAP/TOP.

A past president of the British Computer Society and from 1975-80 the Director of the National Computing Centre (NCC), David Firnberg has been in the forefront of the practical application of information technology for over 30 years.

Presented at HIGH-TECH BUILDINGS 87: Online Publications, Pinner, UK, 1987

## DEFINING THE SUBJECT

If only we did not always slap labels onto concepts, we might stand some chance of understanding what we are all talking about, or at least all talk about the same thing at the same time!

This overview is about two such labels:

- High Tech (or is it Hitec) Buildings

- Intelligent Buildings

For the purpose of this paper I am using the following definitions:

### High Tech Buildings

This is a building designed to accommodate a "high technology" manufacturing organisation where the requirement is for mixed offices, research, manufacturing and assembly facilities, involving a high proportion of scientific or other professional staff.

### Intelligent Buildings

These are buildings which contain within them considerable "built-in" support facilities, both for building controls and to provide services to the occupants.

A high tech building may or may not be an intelligent building; that is to say, it may just be a shell into which the occupants place their own services, or it may be an intelligent building containing the bulk of these services as part of the package that is sold or leased to an occupant.

It is generally thought that "science" or "technology parks" contain a high proportion of both high tech buildings and intelligent buildings, and it is true that such developments attract these types of building, but a "high tech" building does not necessarily contain "high tech" workers, nor of course do all high tech workers work in high tech buildings. The same could perhaps be said about intelligent buildings and intelligent workers!

## HIGH TECH BUILDINGS

The high tech appearance of a building does not imply
that it is in fact a high tech building.  High tech does
not relate to what a building looks like, but to basic
elements of its structure, and the flexibility of usage
it allows.  The key elements that are normally found
are:

- a ground floor providing ready access for service
  access, ground floor loadings sufficient for
  heavy plant or storage, a good basic working
  height, and ample provision for power
  communication cables and other services

- upper floors providing high standard, flexible
  office/laboratory type accommodation, requiring
  flexible environmental and service facilities.

The surroundings are also important to the success of a
high tech building.  It is normally visually attractive,
well landscaped and provided with ample car parking
space.

However, these features of themselves do not necessarily
make a succesful (ie lettable!) building.  A number of
factors work against their success and need to be faced.

The target market is thought to be young, entrepreneurial
high tech companies, but the institutional arrangements
can often deter such companies.  Three aspects in
particular cause difficulties:

- the requirement for a young company to enter into
  a long lease

- the requirement to provide evidence of a
  continuous period of profitable operations, or
  to find a suitable guarantor

- the requirement for cash hungry, young growth
  companies to find an escrow deposit, often
  amounting to 12 months rental.

High tech buildings, like fast sports cars, may appeal
to the young, but more often can only be afforded by the
middle-aged!

Location remains the all important factor. A bad
building in the right location is of far more value
than a good building in the wrong location. Factors
influencing the choice of location include:

- the availability of appropriately skilled people

- ready motorway access to airports and major
  cities, Heathrow and London.

A few of the major provincial Science Parks, such as
Cambridge Lane, succeeded away from major industrial
centres. For this to happen there does need to be some
special attractions, such as the skills, facilities and
cultural facilities found in an academic centre. An
isolated Science Park lacking this sort of support is
unlikely to succeed.

Initially, as with any new fashion, demand exceeds
supply. However as the suppliers realise there is a
demand, they over react and we are now reaching the
stage when supply exceeds demand. This is good news for
the potential occupiers, and developers with badly
located high tech buildings are unlikely to be able to
command the high rents which fueled their investment
decisions.

INTELLIGENT BUILDINGS

The "intelligent" or "smart" building is currently a
fashionable topic about which there is much discussion.
However, there is also a great deal of confusion and
uncertainty about what it is.

There are a number of related terms such as "smart
building", "automated building" and "integrated
building" that tend to be used synonymously and
interchangeably. The semantic difficulties are
compounded by the often direct association, particularly
in the USA, with "shared tenant services", which are
generally assumed to occupy some variety of intelligent
building.

The intelligent building in its various guises involves
a blend of hardware, software and services applied to
the converging technologies of controls, computing and
communications within a building.

The concepts originated in the USA and came to the fore with the deregulation of AT & T, which created a climate of confusion on services felt by users, and strong marketing by vendors wishing to capitalise on apparent business opportunities. There have been a number of bullish independent market forecasts, yet some powerful companies have entered the market, and then withdrawn.

The situation is complex. There are various constituent markets; for example, there is the market for intelligent buildings as a complete entity, but there is also the market for the cabling within them, for the environmental control system, for central communication facilities, for installation services and so on.

There are external factors which significantly affect the market for intelligent buildings and take the form of opportunities and constraints for any company entering this marketplace, some of which are defined below.

## Technological Developments

There are a number of areas in which developments could well affect the degree and nature of the intelligence in a building. These include:

- cable (including fibre optics)
- PABXs, LANs, and the integration of voice and data
- value added and other external network services, notably CENTREX
- building controls
- building materials (especially cladding).

## Standards

The existence of equipment and communication standards, or the lack of them, will exert a strong influence on the viability of the intelligent building. Agreed standards and the existence of conforming products will reduce substantially the uncertainties currently prevalent in the IT industry. The climate for investment in intelligent buildings would be dramatically improved by clarifying the building cabling situation in particular.

The work of the ISO and progress in implementing the Open Systems Interconnect (OSI) seven layer model is especially significant.

## Regulations

In the USA the deregulation of AT & T gave particular impetus to "intelligent" building developments in general, and to shared tenant services (STS) in particular. Regulations in the USA allow third parties to sell on capacity and thereby sharing of PABXs among tenants and the provision of value added network services such as optimal call charge routing. Tele-communications have been the dominant revenue earner in STS buildings.

In the UK British Telecom has lost its monopoly and the liberalisation of telecoms is already well advanced. The UK will probably have the most liberalised tele-communications network in the world by the 1990s. OFTEL plays a key role in influencing the pace and direction of regulatory changes in the UK. Issues include integrated wiring for exchange and direct lines, hybrid wiring for voice and data applications, and value added network services.

## Life Cycles

A dichotomy in the provision of "intelligent" buildings is the contrasting life cycle timescales of constituent elements.

The building shell may have a life of 15 to 50 years, whilst IT equipment has a life expectancy of from 3 to 7 years. The building itself may take up to 5 years from drawing board to completion. The merger of these disparate timeframes will present difficulties to providers of "intelligent" buildings.

Of course, an intelligent building does not have to be a new building. It is easier to build intelligence into a new building, as long as the developer has specified this and the architect has designed for it; however most frequently intelligence is incorporated into an existing building during its refurbishment.

The findings of the original ORBIT study in 1982-3 on criteria with which to assess the degree of intelligence in a building as reported by Francis Duffy, hold good today. The key items are:

- capacity - the degree to which an office building today is able to accommodate electronic technology and its consequences

- adaptability - how easy is it to effect changes in the existing building fabric

- buildability - how easy is to to carry out substantial retrofits especially in mechanical and electrical services

- manageability - how simple and cost effective is it to manage and maintain an office building through time.

An important driving force behind the requirement for intelligence to be part of an office building is that the pattern of demand is shifting from organisations that are fairly static, to less predictable, more rapidly changing users.

In order to respond to these new needs offices must provide:

- more servicing capacity

- more adaptability

- more responsiveness to individual needs

- more responsiveness to social and corporate needs.

The new office may be very different to the multi-storied, simple, evenly serviced, multi-use structures invented in Chicago one hundred years ago and still being proposed today.

Intelligence has to be paid for. For a developer to incorporate a high degree of intelligence in a speculative building, and charge commensurate rents, is a risky process. However a developer who does not make adequate provision for intelligence to be added to a building is even more at risk. It is already cheaper to demolish and rebuild a 1960 spec office than to try and refurbish it. Basic requirements are for ample risers, generous provision for horizontal distribution, and for

the interface between the vertical and horizontal.
Finely zoned air conditioning and individually
controllable lighting are also required.

The property market, and those who service it, tend to
veer between the conservative attitude that claims that
yesterday's offices lasted 100 years, so why should
tomorrow be any different, to enthusiastic espousal of
the latest fashion for comprehensive intelligence (and
high rents). All should seek for a middle road but,
without question, intelligence is required in today's
offices. Developers need to specify the requirement for
intelligence, architects need to design to accommodate
intelligence, and users need to demand intelligence.

# Will the American experience be repeated in the UK?

Susan A Hawkins
Programme Coordinator
ERA Technology Ltd
England

The United States leads the world in the field of intelligent buildings. Many questions have arisen concerning the commercial success of intelligent buildings in America, and the potential market for similar developments in the UK. This paper summarises the issues which have been highlighted during a recent multi-sponsorship study of the potential market for intelligent buildings in Britain.

Susan Hawkins has been with the Marketing Group of ERA Technology for four years. During this period she has participated in several marketing studies in the field of building services. Her most recent project has been an investigation of the UK market for Intelligent Buildings.

Presented at HIGH-TECH BUILDINGS 87: Online Publications, Pinner, UK, 1987

ERA Technology has recently conducted a study which has compared the performance of a sample of American intelligent buildings, and the experience of their users, with the current and foreseen requirements of building users in the UK. The research programme has included field work in the United States and an extensive series of interviews in the UK, with representatives of property development companies, construction companies, consulting engineers, architects, contractors, system suppliers, and building owners and occupiers.

An "intelligent" building may be defined as one that takes the three key pieces of the electronic infrastracture of a building - the controls, the communications and the information processing - and brings them all to the most efficient level. All these systems and services should be considered at the earliest design stages, in order to achieve a flexible and efficient design.

The environment in an intelligent building is controlled by a Building Management System (BMS). Fire, security and lighting control systems may either be independent of the BMS, stand alone systems which are interfaced with the BMS or may be facilities which the BMS itself offers. Data and voice communications are usually based on the use of a PBX and may also require the provision of Local Area Networks. The PBX may be interfaced with the BMS. Telephone lines can be dedicated as communications links between the central processing unit of the BMS and intelligent outstations responsible for the control of individual plant rooms or specific items of plant. The concept of combining all voice, data and building management communications requirements on to a single data highway may become increasingly attractive.

The provision of mechanical and electrical services is greatly affected by decisions concerning the present and likely future requirements for communications systems and information processing. Due to the need for cabling in the automated office, a greater riser capacity is required. The volume allowed must exceed initial requirements in order for the building to be able to efficiently accommodate changes in office automation over its life span. Distributed vertical communications ducts will reduce the horizontal cable runs required, facilitating the addition of new stations and changes in location of existing ones. Air conditioning plant must have adequate capacity for the possible future installation of extra computer suites, or alternatively additional plant space must be allocated.

## Intelligent Buildings in the United States

In the United States the specification of building services, controls and communication systems is coordinated by a design team which includes representatives of the consulting engineers and system suppliers from the earliest design stage. If the building is to be occupied by the owners, the company's own engineers and telecommunications manager may be present on the design team. In the case of a speculative development, a major tenant may have agreed to take a certain amount of space before design work commences, and in this case the anchor tenant's representatives may form part of the design team. In this way the provision of services and control systems are coordinated and integrated with the building design in order to achieve optimum results.

Office buildings in the United States often total between 50,000 and 100,000 square metres of floor space. In speculative, multi-tenant developments there has been a trend towards the provision of Shared Tenant Services Schemes (STSS) defined as "the provision of on-site centralised technology and services that can be shared by all tenants and that serve to enhance tenant productivity or reduce costs". Providers of these services are often subsidiaries of property developers, suppliers of building management systems, or large telecommunications companies. The most important service to be provided to tenants is long distance carrier services, generally at a discounted rate. Other services may include:

o   telephone rental
o   use of message centre
o   conference rooms
o   use of a central computer
o   photocopying and printing
o   rental of personal computers
o   installation of local area networks.

Provision of Shared Tenant services in the United States has been made possible by the deregulation of telecommunications by a series of rulings. The most important of these was the decision to allow any company to buy long-distance carrier services at wholesale rates and retail to end users.

The market for intelligent buildings in the United States is vendor/technology driven by the computer and telecommunications industries and the HVAC control and emergency and security system suppliers. The American commercial building sector is over-built, with typical vacancy rates of 26% in Houston and 11% in Washington. Building "intelligence" is used by developers to enhance property in order to attract and retain tenants.

Energy management facilities provided by Building Management Systems are valued by building owner-occupiers, but are not fully used in speculative multi-tenant buildings. This is due to the fact that tenants are generally charged a flat rate for energy, proportional to the floor space occupied, irrespective of their actual energy consumption. As a result tenants have no incentive to save energy. Building operators who would benefit most from a reduction in energy use are reluctant to shed HVAC loads or control lighting zones in tenant-occupied space, in case this should cause the tenant to seek alternative accommodation at the end of what may be a short lease – typically only five years.

The Intelligent Buildings Institute in Washington is concerned that the term "Intelligent Building" is often misused and misunderstood, and has put forward a new draft definition as follows:

"An Intelligent Building is one which integrates various systems to effectively manage resources in a coordinated mode to maximise:

° occupant performance
° investment and operating cost savings
° flexibility "

It is intended to devise benchmarks by which the degree of building intelligence can be described either in terms of the development's success in meeting the aims described in the definition, or by examining the systems and facilities provided.

While agreeing broadly with this definition I would query the validity of introducing the concept of integration. Our survey has indicated a certain amount of user resistance towards the integration of HVAC control, fire systems and security systems. Many users prefer to interface discrete systems which can stand alone in the event of the failure of any other system. Some building operators, having previously used a Building Management System for control of all services, would now prefer separate systems, which they feel are less vulnerable to system failure, and these may be interfaced with the Building Management System. An intelligent building should aim to meet present and future user requirements, and if such a minimal level of integration of systems provides what is felt to be the most satisfactory solution, a property with such an "interfaced" system should not be excluded from the intelligent building category.

It has been estimated that the development cost of an intelligent building is between 8 and 10% higher than the cost of a traditional structure. In the case of an owner occupied building some of this cost can be justified by resulting energy savings. The provision of adequate cable ways and plant space will give the necessary flexibility to facilitate the installation of new computer suites, and replacement or extension of communications systems throughout the building's life. This will result in a reduction in cost of such work and will give a more satisfactory result. In addition to more tangible benefits the importance of the building's image should not be underestimated.

In the United States, developers of speculative buildings hope to reduce the time taken for all the space to be occupied, by the introduction of building intelligence. This is important in an over-built market. The extra cost incurred in the construction of such a building is recovered from the tenants who pay a premium for the facilities which are provided.

Benefits to the tenants include:

° no capital investment
° maintenance and security staff are not required
° a small company can use systems which it could not otherwise afford.

When a shared tenant service scheme is available tenants enjoy a further reduction in capital investment by leasing office automation equipment.

In general tenants receive a more prompt service from the building operator, in the event of system breakdown, or changes in requirements for communications systems, than they would from the local service providers, and they are spared the responsibility of coordinating the work.

## UK Requirements

There are some major differences between the market for intelligent buildings in the United States and the potential market for similar developments in the UK. One of the most obvious is one of scale, with most buildings in the UK being considerably smaller than their US counterparts. This will be particularly important in the provision of shared tenant services which, in America, are not usually considered viable as a source of profit for buildings of less than 50,000 square metres.

UK building operators appear to be more concerned with energy saving than American organisations and projected pay back periods are an important consideration in the selection of building management systems. Communications systems are already important in the financial services sector and for companies manufacturing products for office automation. These organisations recognise the need for sufficient cable space. Some other organisations accept that they may have an increasing need in the future and are prepared to allocate necessary space.

Many building owners and occupiers in the UK are confused by the term "Intelligent Building". It suggests at least a degree of building services automation to most people. However, organisations which do not, at present, make extensive use of office automation, are not concerned by the implications for communications systems and would not consider the provision of space and services for future computer suites necessary.

There are signs of a gradual change in specification procedures in Britain. An increasing number of developments are coordinated by project managers. Specifications of building systems are generally still equipment based and prepared by consulting engineers and contractors at a late stage in building design. However, many organisations within the construction industry acknowledge the benefits of the "design team" approach, as employed in the United States.

One building operator has written detailed manuals to guide the specification of systems for their buildings, and these are consulted during the initial stages with systems and services being coordinated into the initial building design.

The survey has indicated varying attitudes towards the integration of systems, with some users integrating fire and security systems with building management systems and others preferring separate systems. There are companies within the UK who are, or could shortly be, able to provide an integrated building package and this will not be an obstacle to the growth of the industry in the UK.

Some building operators have stated that they would like to be able to obtain all necessary building systems from one supplier in order to overcome problems in system compatibility. Another important advantage is seen to be the possibility of arranging a single maintenance contract, avoiding possible problems concerning responsibility for complex systems. This is a need to which the industry should be able to respond, and which could well foster a more coordinated approach to building design, with suppliers playing a more prominent role on the design team.

## Shared Tenant Services Schemes in the UK

The issue of Shared Tenant Services Schemes in the UK is complicated by the fact that the British Telecom monopoly over the provision of tele-communications has only recently been abolished. There can be little doubt that over the next few years there will be increasingly strong competition from other network operators. This may bring about a situation similar to that which exists in the United States, where attractive financial benefits can be offered to tenants participating in a Shared Tenant Services Scheme. The other aspect of an STSS, that of management and maintenance of the buildings and its services, already provides an opportunity to the UK building industry. Some organisations have expressed a reluctance towards sharing communications facilities, on the grounds of data security, and many would not wish to share computer facilities. However, in the United States it has often been possible to overcome such objections or to compromise by the provision of local area networks to meet the specific needs of some individual tenants.

## The future for Intelligent Buildings in the UK

The UK marketplace is more conservative than that in the United States. Tax laws in America, only recently modified, have made investment in property attractive, resulting in the present level of overbuilding. This has encouraged developers to try new ideas and to experiment with building intelligence. It would be far more difficult for suppliers to drive the UK market by the push of technology in the same way. However, partly due to the influence of American organisations who are active in the UK, the level of awareness of building operators is being increased. Although cautious, organisations are investigating the benefits to the occupier of the intelligent building, and companies seeking a prestigious image for their corporate headquarters may well establish the market for intelligent buildings in the UK.

# Investing in high-tech buildings

Michael J. Boggis
Managing Director
Allied Dunbar Property Funds Limited

The recent changes in the UK financial industry have resulted in a
major shift in the financing of property away from the institutions
and towards the banks and property companies. New forms of debt to
finance the purchase of property are appearing with lessons being
learned from the US property market. However, the new look UK
property market although novel in approach still comes with its own
inherent risk.

Michael J. Boggis is a chartered Surveyor and Managing Director with
the largest group of unit linked property funds in the United Kingdom.

Presented at HIGH-TECH BUILDINGS 87: Online Publications, Pinner, UK, 1987

## Recent Additions to Previous Sources of Finance

1.  Rentals derived from long leases of commercial property provide an excellent match for fixed interest securities, and mortgages are now available at a minimum of 1½% or more above the interest rate of gilts.

2.  Banks have been seeking an ever increasing slice of the property lending market particularly in major property developments e.g. Broadgate.

3.  A non-recourse loan is now commonplace, as lenders have been able to spread their risk by syndication.

4.  Stock markets have climbed at a spectacular rate causing U.K. institutional fund managers to switch out of property and into equities.

5.  The British have also learnt some lessons from the U.S. property market.

    Put all these changes together and the result is a major shift in financing away from the institutions and towards the banks and property companies using various forms of debt to finance purchases of property:-

    (i)   Single property companies with quoted equity and securitised loan stock, e.g. the flotation of Billingsgate last year and Letinvest this year.

    (ii)  A greater use of partnerships often between two or three property companies.

    (iii) PINCS.

    (iv)  Single property trusts.

    (v)   Authorised property unit trusts.

    The SPT is simpler in legal structure than a PINC and unlike a PINC it provides the investor with an interest in land in the form of one class of units or shares which enables the new investor to benefit from capital allowances. A PINC is a "stapled security" comprising two elements:-

(i) An unsecured contractural obligation issued by the financial intermediary which gives the investor the right to participate in the income from the building and any capital gain arising from its disposal.

(ii) An ordinary share in the company managing the property.

## What Will the Market Look Like?

Discussions are in hand with the Stock Exchange with a view to their running the market and handling flotations in a similar manner to the existing Unlisted Securities Market with dealings taking place on screens communicating with a central computer.

## What are the Right Market Conditions?

On the one hand, the prospective yield to the investor needs to be sufficiently attractive to lure him away from other forms of investment, including direct property investment.

On the other hand, the prospective price to be received by the vendor needs to be one and probably several bids higher than the current open market value of the whole property being sold as otherwise the risk of an unsuccessful flotation would be unacceptable to the vendor.

Furthermore, the initial trading of the units needs to be at an attractive premium to encourage investors to invest a second time round in further flotations.

## What Type of Property Might be Offered?

I believe single tenant large buildings will be extremely boring investments and may eventually trade at discounts. Multi let properties, having scattered rent reviews and lease expiry dates are better and whereas developments are thought by some to be inappropriate for a new market as they are risky, it is the opportunity to take on risk situations with the facility to spread that risk which most attracts me to the market - otherwise it could be a bore.

A major high tech development could be attractive to a wide range of investors if each investor can just risk a relatively small sum of money.

## High Tech

High tech is no more than a hybrid between offices and industrial buildings.

1. ### Location:

   Always the principle consideration for both tenants and the investor. Essential ingredients include good motorway connections, air and rail links, proximity to good housing, supply of staff, schooling and preferably a university or polytechnic nearby with a relevant industrial speciality.

2. ### Position :

   Prominence and individual corporate identity charisma are important.

3. ### Flexibility and Practicality of the building is essential.

4. ### Proximity to other Plants and Customers:

5. ### Cost and Lease Terms:

   Tenants' options to break leases are becoming less frequent. From the investors point of view, options to break represent a material disadvantage having perhaps a 20% adverse impact on capital value which is not offset by a comparable, or justifiably even greater, increase in rental offered by tenants.

## Investment Attributes of High Tech Properties

(a) Location : Outside a 10 mile band inside/outside the M25 or beyond the A1(M) at Stevenage, the M1 at Hemel Hempstead, the M4 at Newbury or the M3 at Basingstoke high tech developments are generally uneconomic.

(b) Rental Levels : Broadly speaking, high tech rents comprise the sum of:-

   (1) The local air conditioned, town centre, office rental value applied to the office content

Plus

(2) The local industrial rental value applied to the industrial content.

(c) <u>Yields</u>: These tend to range from 7% to 9% depending upon location, covenant, length of lease and quality of the building.

(d) <u>Development Feasibility Studies</u>

(i) Developments outside the M25/"Golden Triangle" regions as generally uneconomic as the high construction cost, at about £55 per square foot basic building cost (50% air conditioned offices, 50% ground floor industrial shell), necessitates a minimum rental of around £7.50 per square foot (gross) to achieve a 20% profit margin (arguably a slim margin, for a relatively speculative form of development). Other locations do not support such rental figures being achieved.

(ii) A major business park involves exceptionally large quantities of capital to develop. Profitability can be quickly reversed to a loss as interest charges escalate on a major site acquired at a fixed price when there is a slowdown in letting conditions.

The alternative is to buy sites through options to purchase at open market value.

(iii) Probably 50% of high tech buildings are sold to occupiers.

(e) <u>Letting Market Conditions</u>

As high tech is only about five years old, the depth of demand from occupiers is still difficult to quantify. Matching individual building sizes is particularly difficult.

(f) <u>Prospective Changes to the Use Classes Orders</u>

(i) The bonus of business class user to rental values is probably less than 10%.

(ii)  A change in yield rating would probably increase the years purchase multiple by 10% and this together with an increased rental value could increase capital values by up to 20%.

(g)  <u>Obsolescence</u>

It is a fair bet that obsolescence in high tech would be at a higher rate than in normal offices.

<u>Conclusion</u>

High tech caters for the more upmarket space requirements of industrial tenants and provides a useful additional branch for property investment. Demand by tenants has been good, but is currently patchy, and there may be a reasonable upside potential to come if a new Business Class is permitted under the Use Classes Orders.

# Does the future of high-tech buildings depend on our ability to manage them?

D.R. PENGILLY
Group Manager
Matthew Hall Mechanical & Electrical Engineers Limited
Great Britain

The future development of high-tech and intelligent buildings provides designers and engineers with a new and exciting series of challenges. However, the high-tech/intelligent building movement in the United States appears to have drawn itself a deep breath whilst deciding what to do next. The ability to successfully manage and occupy these new buildings demands a different range of skills, wider, broader and demanding more depth than before. It is important that the need for these skills be recognised otherwise many high-tech buildings will face a difficult future.

Rex Pengilly is a Group Manager with the Maintenance Division of Matthew Hall Mechanical and Electrical Engineers Ltd. He has been actively involved in building automation and the management of building services maintenance over the past eighteen years. He is a Fellow of the Institute of Sales & Marketing Management, a Fellow of the Association of Facilities Managers and an Associate Member of the Institute of Energy.

Presented at HIGH-TECH BUILDINGS 87: Online Publications, Pinner, UK, 1987

## INTRODUCTION

The concept of an intelligent or high-tech building is very much a product of the present decade.

The first "intelligent" building was completed in 1981 in the United States and it seems that ever since people have been trying to define exactly what the expression "intelligent" or "high-tech" building means.

Clearly it means different things to different people. In some cases, a radical or high-tech approach to the architectural design is all that is required for a project to assume the mantle of a high-tech building. In others, just its location and future commercial or industrial use will suffice. Obviously neither of these examples can be sustained in terms of the building being intelligent or high-tech but serve to show how the expression has been mis-used.

Last year, in my paper to this conference, I stated that in my view an intelligent or high-tech building was one where the Building Management System, the Communications System and the Information Management System were integral to the building and where these systems served to enhance the well-being and productivity of the occupants. This appears to be in line with the recent draft definition issued by the Intelligent Building Institute in the U.S.A., although they go further to include Investment, Operating Cost Savings and Flexibility to be characteristics of an intelligent or high-tech building.

This feature of Operating Costs is of paramount importance and one that is seldom brought under the spotlight early enough in the design programme.

Why is it of such importance, you may ask? Well, in the first case a recent study in America indicated that an intelligent building costs somewhere between 8 and 10% more to construct than a traditional one. So if the concept is going to be fiscally viable, then it must be attractive in revenue rather than capital terms. However, here in the U.K., we can find numerous examples where tenants are paying increased, even over-the-odds, premiums for high-tech space.

In short, to date the only justification in occupying such space often appears to be that it either suits or boosts the corporate image.

This need not be so. If an integrated approach is adopted
to managing the systems within a high-tech or intelligent
building, then the cost of residence need be not more than
in a traditional building - indeed, it may well be less.

It is clear that in the future all buildings will be intelligent
or high-tech to a varying degree, if only in terms of their
energy efficiency, communications, business system - data
handling, fire and safety provisions. There is a move towards
intelligent buildings that is gaining credibility worldwide,
albeit slower than the industry itself would like and, as
a result, building owners, developers and facilities managers
must formulate a strategy to anticipate the consequences of
this phenomenon rather than being left in its wake.

## OPERATION AND MAINTENANCE AT THE DESIGN STAGE

There have been instances where "intelligent" buildings have
failed to live up to the initial hopes and expectations. The
reasons for this are complex. However, one clear lesson has
come from these cases. That is, in order to succeed a defined
plan incorporating an integrated strategy of some kind must
be followed. This can be further developed into just "How
will the building be managed in the long term?"

At present "intelligent" buildings rely on a series of separate
but advanced technologies.

The sooner these can be brought together and the management
strategy developed the better.

These technologies are seen in the various systems serving
an intelligent building and were highlighted in the introduction.
Each of these systems has an impact on the other at every
stage of the building's development.

Initially they can be seen in generic terms as

*       an Environmental System

*       a Business System

*       a Communications System

Currently these are dealt with on an individual basis with
very little reference or planned integration. Indeed, the level
of skills and expertise is different in each case and as a
result it is initially difficult to see how they could be brought
under a combined umbrella of single source responsibility.

These technologies, however, must be brought together somehow and managed efficiently to provide the owner/tenant with the necessary operational 'bottom line' performance if the additional capital investment in an intelligent building is to be considered worthwhile. The problem is that there are many new questions to be addressed before these elements can be successfully managed.

There have been attempts to achieve such an objective both in the United States and here in the United Kingdom.

America has seen a variety of approaches.

*        The set-up of specialist companies to bring together different skills.

*        The large company offering a turnkey package addressing all areas within their own corporate structure.

*        The development of Shared Tenant Services giving a Value Added Service to the individually specified and installed services, throughout multi-tenanted buildings.

In the United Kingdom the development has followed a less defined approach, each of the elements being designed separately and handled as an entity in its own right. Similarly when the building passes from design to construct and on to occupancy, the manner in which they are treated reflects the fractional nature of the service industries.

This leaves the responsibility and therefore the risk and the associated costs very much with the tenant or client organisation.

If the operation and maintenance of the services and systems within a high-tech or intelligent building can be viewed in an integrated manner at the design stage, it enables the building owner/developer to measure his requirements against the trade-offs that may be gained by viewing the building as a whole throughout its expected life. In this way the operational costs or overall cost in use can be significantly reduced as a result of the economies of scale involved.

The problem that has to be resolved is: How can all these requirements be accurately forecast at the outset and how can they be successfully integrated one with each other?

The total turnkey approach offered by a single company demands a very high level of control of the specification and as a result may well create a degree of resentment or fear in closing off options too early. Indeed it may well be difficult to see how one company alone can be a market leader in all of the necessary market skills and products.

## AN INTEGRATED MANAGEMENT APPROACH

If the prospect of managing and operating "intelligent" buildings indicates that it is too broad for a single company to handle successfully, then it likely follows that it is similarly going to be difficult for traditional facilities management techniques to be successful.

Let us look for a minute at what is involved in terms of engineering knowledge alone. Most companies are not in themselves sophisticated energy users and therefore need to look outside of their primary business expertise to find the more specialised resource they need. Similarly, in terms of communications management, how many companies can truly claim to be abreast of all the current developments and changes that are taking place? Properly managed communications can have an impact on the success of a business enterprise and are of such strategic importance that they should be treated as part of the corporate plan. Generally business system management is directly related to a company's or organisation's primary activity and as such to the fore of the previously mentioned areas. As a result, it is better served. However, the recent emergence of third party maintenance companies dealing in hardware and software maintenance indicates that perhaps all was not too well before, even in this area. Although just by being there, they create another headache. The choice becomes even wider than before, performance can vary tremendously, selection demands insight, care and consumes valuable management time as another factor is added to the equation.

So, if it is logical to adopt an integrated approach to managing these new buildings, does it make financial sense?

Looking at the energy commitment and the operation of the environmental systems in the first instance, it has already been said that many companies and organisations are not sophisticated energy users having within themselves the financial and technical skills to maximise the current technological advantages and this is spite of the fact that in many instances their energy bill represents a very large proportion of their controllable costs.

However, in endeavouring to get the energy usage under control, what criteria is used to judge whether the current performance is good or bad?

If the base figure is twice what it should be, then saving 20 or 30% is not really a major achievement - it is little more than the identification of obvious waste. Similarly, if by saving energy the equilibrium in terms of space comfort conditions is disturbed, the resulting interruption and dissatisfaction will soon eliminate the benefit of any expected savings.

It should also be noted that many energy management strategies are expensive in terms of the life of the mechanical plant serving the environmental services. Where this is not recognised and the energy management is not linked or integrated into the maintenance programme the direct impact each has on the other can mean that money hopefully saved in one area is lost in another. Moreover, where these functions are not closely linked under a common responsibility in the form of a performance contract on the basis of a defined and maintained comfort condition within the occupied space, then whichever area is not specifically addressed by the individual contract become the reponsibility of the client who picks up the associated costs.

This is usually as a result of the well-known phenomenon that when something goes wrong everyone tends to blame everyone else and with no common or single source responsibility the Client very quickly becomes "piggy in the middle".

Within intelligent or high-tech buildings, the level of performance of the environmental systems is greater than has been traditionally expected and so the likelihood of problems must be greater.

## OVERCOMING THE APPARENT SKILL SHORTAGES

Generally the need for an adequate supply of skilled labour is well recognised as being a national problem and there are signs that this awareness is stimulating action.

However, if we are to cope with the increasing demands of operating and managing high-tech or intelligent buildings, we need a much broader education for building designers. If we just go on educating ourselves as engineers and architects instead of considering building design on the basis of benefiting other people, then it seems to me we are ignoring the real reason for the building, which is to seek and provide the technical, social and economic solutions.

Taking up the view that an intelligent building should be flexible and able to adapt to the changing need of the occupants rather than the other way around serves to support this view. Therefore we must turn away from the perceived requirement that building design is the vocation of the architect alone with some help from structural engineers and surveyors and move to the more integrated approach at the earliest possible opportunity. This must incorporate a wide spread of engineering, operational and general management skills.

Parents, school leavers and career masters do not take into account the prospects offered by building environmental engineering and in most cases are wholly unaware of the broader spread of opportunities that go to make up what is now beginning to be recognised as facilities management.

Unfortunately the same could be said of our academic institutions for the number of them offering full-time undergraduate courses is very small. Even more pitiful is the number of suitable applicants they are able to attract between them.

This lack of skilled staff is not just restricted to the professional level. In earlier years the major manufacturing companies and contractors offered carft and technician apprenticeships and it was from these that the bulk of the industry's current workforce emanated. However, with the effect of the recession in the early 1970's, many of these training programmes were decimated, with the result that the workforce was stabilised almost to the point of stagnation in the ensuing years. Today many companies in our industry can look to their staff to see that the average age of those they employ is considerably higher than it was ten years ago.

Fortunately steps have been taken to redress this balance and a number of worthwhile training schemes both at the undergraduate and apprentice ends of the scale are again underway. However, it will be some years before their full effect will be felt by the industry.

Another area which affects the availability of skilled staff reflects the change in operation of many of the high-tech buildings serving the financial services market which are now envisaging twenty-four hour operation to keep in touch with world markets and therefore require a full shift operation. Many companies and organisations within the financial services sector have recognised this potential need and are gearing up to attract their share of suitable people. Unfortunately they draw these people from the existing pool of industry trained staff and offer no direct contribution themselves to future replenishment and this is sad when one considers that in most cases they could well afford to support their own or nationally recognised training schemes.

Moving on from the specific area of environmental engineering into the broader field of facilities management, it is clear that whatever career background a facilities manager may have - be it data processing, communications or whatever - he does need to understand the strategic implications of support services. It is the facilities manager's responsibility to not only install the equipment and see that it works, but he is responsible to look after the user's comfort in terms of the layout and environment. It is necessary to be able to communicate with architects, builders, communications, environmental, hardware and software engineers.

Being able to do all this and fit it all in is quite a feat, especially when you contemplate what is entailed and the implication of what happens should it go wrong.

At the moment, the need for facilities managers is being recognised but little is being done to provide the necessary training and education. More often than not, the development of these skills is left to occur on an ad hoc basis.

Clearly there is a need to provide the right recruitment and training prospects across the range of technologies involved if we are to attract the right sort of people to operate and manage the buildings we are currently designing and constructing. If we don't, we will end up giving people buildings and systems for which they have no concept of how they work or what they are supposed to do.

## CONCLUSION

A secure business plan involving at the outset the buildings operational requirements will enhance the chances of success for a high-tech "intelligent" building in the medium or longer term.

If a turnkey operation offered by a single company seems too restrictive or the width of experience too great for traditional facilities management to cope with, what other options exist?

It is my belief that we will see a development of the "specially set-up" company or organisation as originally occurred in the U.S.A. emerging over here. Not as a single source company in terms of expertise but a group of expert organisations coming together on the basis of a consortium to meet the needs of the "intelligent building" owner/tenant.

Such a grouping would adequately encompass the communication, environmental and business system skills and offer the depth of experience and breadth of resource necessary to make "it" happen for the building owner. Similarly such a grouping can, by the economy of scale it would encompass, minimise the skill shortages that are now apparent.

This would give the building owner a workable single source responsibility for negotiating his design specification and ongoing operational strategy but allowing him the freedom to keep his individual options open. In this context the future of high-tech buildings is very much dependent on us having the skills and management resources to successfully operate them.

31

# Harnessing information technology to manage high-tech buildings

CHRIS M. TURK
Manager
Arthur Andersen & Co. Management Consultants
United Kingdom

High calibre facilities managers and effective information are the key, inseparable components required to ensure efficient and effective management of high-tech buildings. By a facilities manager we mean the person charged with the responsibility for providing an appropriate, cost efficient environment to support the organisation's business.

To assist with the provision of effective information, this paper outlines an approach to identifying the information systems required, by looking at the information needs of the facilities manager. It also discusses the role information technology (IT) can play, capturing and storing facilities management information generated through the design and construction process.

Mr. Turk is a Chartered Civil Engineer and a Manager in Arthur Andersen & Co. Management Consultants, London office. He is responsible for co-ordinating the firm's property/facilities management practice having undertaken several information systems related engagements in this area.

Presented at HIGH-TECH BUILDINGS 87: Online Publications, Pinner, UK, 1987

## 1. Introduction

What's so special about high-tech buildings that justifies the use
of information technology (IT) for their management?  To answer this
fundamental question requires a consideration of what is meant by a
high-tech building and the changes which have led to the need for
high-calibre management techniques over the period the building is
occupied.

The definition of a high-tech building differs depending on who you
talk to.  The architect traditionally considers a high-tech building
to be one which is constructed of technically innovative materials
such as silicon glazing, or incorporates sophisticated construction
methods such as pre-fabricated modules.  The mechanical and
electrical engineer considers a building with an automated building
control system as falling in the high-tech category, whereas the
average building user considers the IT installed within the building
is the key criteria for labelling a building high-tech.  For the
purpose of this paper I am classifying a high-tech building as one
which uses IT to control the building (ie. a computer based building
control system, responding to integrated sensors and controls), uses
IT to manage the use of the building, and incorporates IT to support
the business (ie. voice, data, text and graphics processing and
communications).

In recent years, several changes have occured which have contributed
to the birth of the high-tech building and have reinforced the need
for their effective and cost efficient management.  The most notable
being:

- The different life cycles of the different components of todays
  building.  The structural shell and core of todays building is
  generally designed for a life cycle of 50 years or more, whereas
  the building fabric and central services are designed for a life
  of 15-20 years, and fit-out components, such as raised access
  floors and ceiling systems, are often aimed at only 10 years to
  allow planned adaptability.

- The considerable drop in price of technology over the past 10
  years, when equivalent performance is compared.

- The rapid increase in take-up of technology.  In many businesses
  IT has moved from supporting the business to becoming the heart
  of the business as organisations strive to use IT to give them
  competitive advantage in the market place.

- The emphasis on organisational flexibility, ie. the desire of
  large organisations to form and disband teams rapidly to meet
  market needs.

To accommodate these changes and turn them to advantages requires as much managerial skill as the design and construction process itself. In fact increasingly we see the management of the building through live operation i.e. when it is occupied, as the final phase of the project. The management approach to the live operation of the building and the information systems required should be considered and built into the design and construction stages of the high-tech building.

## 2. What's required to manage High-tech Buildings once they are occupied?

High calibre facilities managers and effective information to assist them manage are the key, inseparable components required to ensure efficient and effective use of high-tech buildings. By facilities managers in this context, I am referring to the individuals or small teams responsible for providing the appropriate, controlled environment to support their organisation's business, within senior management's policy and at an economic cost. I refer here and throughout this paper to the responsibility of the owner-occupier or tenant facilities manager(s). The responsibilities of a facilities manager working on behalf of a developer or a building owner would differ in emphasis, but many of the information needs and systems referred to later are relevant to this different role.

Facilities managers must understand their organisation's business and be able to assess the true effect of failure to provide the required environment. They must also understand the technology employed to control the building and be able to interpret and act on the information it provides. I would suggest that there are not that many facilities managers who fit these demanding criteria and that organisations using high-tech buildings will have to look hard to find the appropriate personnel. However providing their facilities manager and his team with the right information from computerised systems is something an organisation can plan for and implement.

## 3. Information Needs

Although volumes of data are supplied by today's automated building control systems there is a danger of being drowned in data but starved of information. There is therefore a need to focus the available data into management information and to consider the provision of other key information provided from other sources, such as:

- The future organisation and space requirements

    . numbers of personnel by seniority and function
    . space standards
    . space requirements

- Information technology strategy

  . systems development projects
  . technical architecture
  . implementation timescales

- Project schedules, budgets and status

- Estimating data

- Facilities management budgets, actuals and forecasts

- Building characteristics

  . physical form (drawings)
  . management's design policy
  . specifications
  . test certificates

- Plant and equipment drawings and specifications

To decide what information is required and how it should be delivered (building control system, other computerised information system or manual) it helps to focus on the information requirements for the property/facilities management area as a whole through the following framework of major business functions.

**Property/Facilities
Management Structure**                                              **Figure 1**

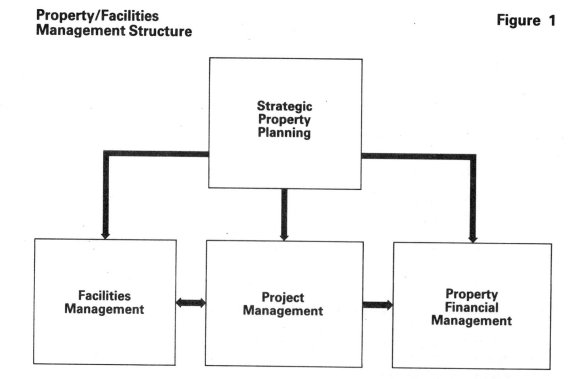

Broadly these major business functions can be defined as:

- <u>Strategic property planning</u>
  - Long term property planning to satisfy the long term business plan of the organisation

- <u>Facilities Management</u>
  - The overall responsibility for making the premises work in accordance with the business needs.

- <u>Project Management</u>
  - The management of a distinct set of activities to achieve a significant end product.  For example the creation of  new facilities by either renovation or new construction.

- <u>Property financial Management</u>
  - The procurement and sale of property and the administration of both residential and commercial leases.

The following diagram (Figure 2) shows a generic set of information needs for each major business function.  These have been built up from several information systems engagements we have performed in the property/facilities management area.

The specific roles and responsibilities of the facilities manager and related functions, such as purchasing, finance and accounting and possibly project management, should be mapped against the information needs to help establish the detailed requirements and to assist in shaping the systems solution.

## Property/Facilities Management
## — Information needs

Figure 2

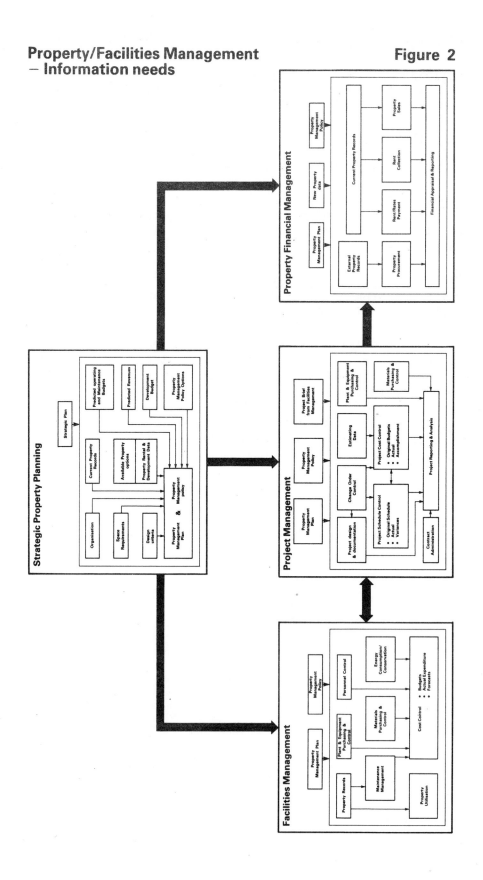

## 4. From where can the information be obtained?

Figure 3 shows the most likely source(s) for each of the major components of the information needs represented in Figure 2. (In the interests of space, the major components have been listed under the most appropriate major business function heading and not repeated.)

INFORMATION SOURCES MATRIX                                    FIGURE 3

| SOURCE OF INFORMATION / INFORMATION NEEDS | 1/THE DESIGN AND CONSTRUCTION PROCESS | 2/AUTOMATED CONTROLS & SENSORS (BUILDING CONTROL SYSTEM) | 3/GENERATED /COLLECTED BY FACILITIES MANAGEMENT | 4/OTHER . External Property Agents . Senior Management . Statutory Authorities |
|---|---|---|---|---|
| **STRATEGIC PROPERTY PLANNING** | | | | |
| 1. Organisation statistics | | | | X |
| 2. Space requirements | | | X | |
| 3. Key property/ building records size, value, etc. | X | | | |
| 4. Building operating budgets and costs, etc. | | | X | |
| 5. Predicted revenues | | | X | |
| 6. Development budgets | | | X | |
| 7. Property management Policy | | | | X |
| **FACILITIES MANAGEMENT** | | | | |
| 8. Building detailed physical shape - drawings | X | | | |
| 9. Building design criteria and material specifications | X | | | |
| 10. Plant and equipment drawings | X | | | |
| 11. Plant and equipment specifications and maintenance data | X | | | |
| 12. Energy consumption | | X | | |
| 13. Property Utilisation | | X | X | |
| **PROJECT MANAGEMENT** | | | | |
| 14. Project budgets and costs | | | X | |
| 15. Project schedules | | | X | |
| 16. Materials, plant and equipment requirements | | | X | |
| 17. Maintenance work orders | | | X | |
| 18. Facilities personnel data | | | X | |
| 19. Estimating data | X | | X | |
| **PROPERTY FINANCIAL MANAGEMENT** | | | | |
| 20. Rents | | | X | |
| 21. Rates | | | X | |
| 22. Charges | | | X | |
| 23. Statutory regulations | | | | X |

Although much of the information required is generated or collected by the facilities management function, a wealth of information on the physical characteristics of the building and its components is generated in the design and construction process. The potential benefits to facilities management of using information technology to capture and manage the flow of information through design and construction, a process we refer to as managing the information pipeline, is only now being realised. Maintenance (of both the building and plant and equipment) and facilities planning/utilisation being the key areas of benefit.

Unfortunately the wealth of information generated through design and construction is not generally stored or structured with the needs of smooth facilities planning and maintenance in mind. As a consequence organisations who are constructing high-tech buildings for their own use are beginning to look hard at ways of gaining tighter control of information generated through the project life cycle to gain the business advantages of effective and efficient operation of the building. However owner-occupier buildings are a small percentage of office developments in London (approximately 12% by floor area in 1986). For the larger percentage of speculative developer/tenant high-tech buildings, the business advantages for managing this information pipeline become divided between building owner and user and hence the issue of who should make the effort (i.e. foot the bill) to control the information pipeline becomes key. Some developers are already seeing the benefits of increased efficiency and effective project management through the co-ordination of design and construction information using available IT. If properly planned, this should leave much of the information required for facilities management available in a structured form on magnetic media.

Only relatively recently have the more advanced IT tools and techniques which the construction industry needs to achieve the control of information through the project life-cycle, begun to emerge in a widely useable and cost effective form. Although many of these solutions particularly in the computer aided design (CAD) area have been available for sometime, the cost has been prohibitive except to large firms, undertaking complex design work, probably of a repetitive nature and forward thinking firms who invested in CAD to increase their work-load capability and gain competitive advantage. Now, however solutions are available at a tenth of the price with probably up to 85% of the functionality.

Perhaps the other factor is the emergence of powerful relational databases which, when coupled with mass storage devices, have the power and sophistication to handle the complex relationships between the many thousands of pieces of data in the design and construction process. These "engineering databases" as they are being termed provide one of the important tools for achieving data integration.

The future should see an increase in the developers and users of high-tech buildings controlling the information pipeline through the use of IT to ensure the information required for efficient and effective management of the building is readily available.

## 5. Property/Facilities Management Systems to satisfy the information needs

The systems solution to provide the facilities manager with the information he needs to manage the completed building is not simple. There is no one package which covers all the information needs discussed in section 3 above. The main application systems which should be considered for the property/facilities management area are shown in figure 4 on the following page, mapped against the framework used to classify the information needs.

The boundaries between the applications are not universally defined. One vendors building control system may also include much of the functions associated with maintenance management. The key is to establish what information really is required and ensure a combination of packaged and custom coded systems deliver the required information in a useable format and in a timescale that allows management to take place.

In addition to the application systems, the key technologies shown on figure 4:

- Computer aided design (CAD)

- End user computing

- Word processing

- Artificial intelligence (expert systems)

are having a big impact in the property/facilities management arena and must be considered when any information systems are being developed.

There is a great deal of interest in artificial intelligence (AI) at present as in many application areas it is moving out of the research laboratories into practical applications. AI systems are programmed in such a way that knowledge is captured and stored as a knowledge base. The system is capable of accessing the knowledge base, diagnosing the problem and suggesting the best course of action. An intelligent building control system, with an AI system reacting to information fed from the various control sensors in the building is now a possibility. If carefully programmed, capturing and using knowledge of experienced facilities managers and mechanical and electrical engineers, the intelligent building

# Property/Facilities Management
## — Application systems

**Figure 4**

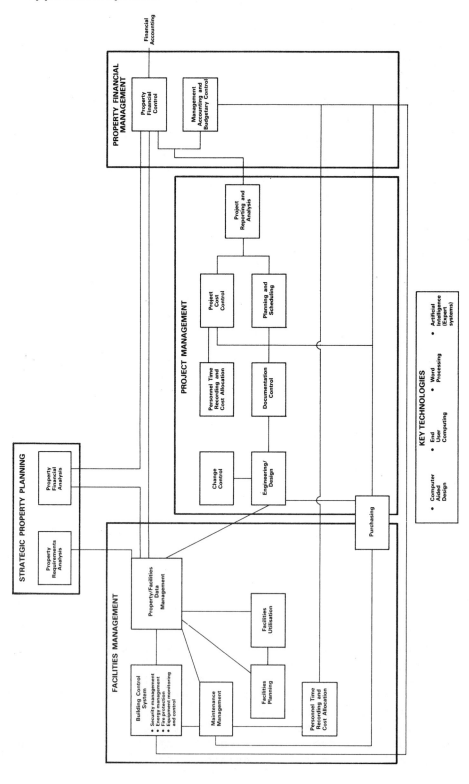

control system can safeguard the high-tech building and its
components 24 hours a day by diagnosing faults, drawing on reserve
equipment and alerting the maintenance team as necessary. Thus
reducing the need to have highly experienced facilities managers and
engineers at the building full time.

## 6. Conclusion

To sort through the technology jungle and arrive at what is really
required out of the wide range of packages, application generators
and today's technologies is clearly not easy. The development of
effective facilities management systems requires well planned
systems integration, which is the pulling together of application
software, hardware and key technologies such as CAD, end user
computing, word processing, etc. Unfortunately, systems integration
doesn't just happen by accident, it requires strategic information
planning and a structured, proven approach to systems development if
the many pitfalls which can occur are to be avoided.

In our view successful property/facilities management is a matter of
understanding the relationships between the organisation, the
facilities required and information technology (IT). The three are
inextricably linked as IT will fundamentally affect the shape of the
organisation which clearly affects the facilities required which in
turn affects the IT which can be installed and delivered to the
organisation, and so on. The process is iterative but without a
shadow of a doubt is currently IT led.

# Using information feedback for energy management

S L Hodkinson, Director
D R Oughton, Director
Oscar Faber Consulting Engineers
UK

This paper describes the application of a comprehensive microprocessor based energy management/control system at the recently completed Administration Centre for a major bank just north of the City of London. All the office complex systems are installed at great expense and their full benefits are never realised. This paper describes ways that these may be achieved.

Steve Hodkinson joined Oscar Faber Consulting Engineers in 1976 and has special interests in controls and energy management systems. He was the Associate responsible for the Royal Bank of Scotland project and has recently been appointed a Director.

Doug Oughton started in the Building Services industry with major Contractors and subsequently joined Oscar Faber Consulting Engineers. He has responsibility for several major projects. Author of several papers on Energy related subjects.

Presented at HIGH-TECH BUILDINGS 87: Online Publications, Pinner, UK, 1987

# 1. Introduction

The effective and energy efficient control of large buildings is increasingly possible as a result of the development of microprocessor based energy management systems.

The pace of development in the application of advanced control and energy management systems to building services is extremely high.

This paper describes the application of microprocessor based technology to the recently completed Administration Centre for a major bank client just to the north of the City of London.

In particular, three main features will be highlighted:

a. Integration of a large number of room temperature controllers with the energy management system. This provides a highly flexible and energy efficient variable air volume air conditioning system to meet the high demands of a modern office.

b. Maximising the benefit of the energy management system with the designers having a continuing involvement with fine tuning the performance of the building via a BT Kilostream link from their offices. This allows the engineers direct access to the actual plant operating conditions and to external climatic and internal conditions.

c. A unique arrangement of linking the energy management system with the designers' energy simulation program. The engineering systems performance, over a range of different controls philosophies, will be simulated through a typical year's weather and operating conditions. Whereas this operation would take many years, by making adjustments to the systems controls on the site, even with the aid of EMS, by simulation it would be completed in a matter of hours.

## 2.   The Royal Bank of Scotland's Building

The case study to which this paper refers is the
recently completed building for the Royal Bank of
Scotland at the Angel, Islington.

The building comprises six floors above ground level
and has an area floor of approximately 30,000 m²
(300,000 ft²).

Facilities are provided for office accommodation, data
processing areas, a clearing department, catering and
recreational facilities.  The building houses 1,400
staff and is arranged around two landscaped courtyards.

The design of the engineering systems has aimed to
combine flexibility for the needs of a variety of
office processes both now and in the future, high
standards of user comfort and maximum control over
energy use.

The office accommodation is air conditioned by variable
air volume systems, supplemented by perimeter natural
convectors.  Air is introduced through ceiling
diffusers integrated with luminaires and arranged
together with power and communication systems to provide
flexibility on a planning module of 1200mm.

A comprehensive energy management system with
distributed intelligence has been installed to control
and monitor all mechanical and electrical systems.
Extensive use has been made of microprocessor based
direct digital control techniques in the control of
the engineering systems.

## 3.   The Energy Management System Configuration

A simplified diagram of how the Energy Management
System is configured within the building is indicated
in Figure 1.

The system utilises stand alone outstations to control
the central plant and this principle has been extended
to incorporate other stand alone systems which
interface with the EMS.

These systems include automatic lighting controls, fire alarms, Halon fire protection systems and an independent room temperature control system associated with the VAV terminal units.

The system includes dynamic colour graphic displays and comprehensive calculations packages.

Figure 1

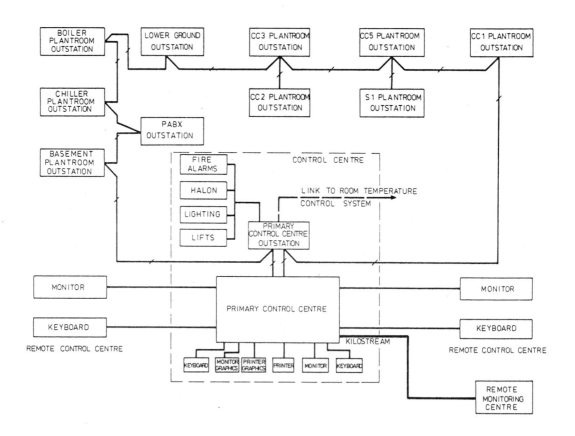

DIAGRAM OF ENERGY MANAGEMENT
SYSTEM

## 4. Room Temperature Controls

The usual method of controlling large variable air volume systems has been to set the supply air temperature either to meet the maximum condition or scheduled from information collected by external sensors. Alternatively, a limited number of strategically placed internal sensors may have been hard wired back to the central plant.

With the increasing use of high heat gain office equipment in buildings, often concentrated in local areas, it is not adequate from controlability or energy aspects to sense average conditions in a large zone. There is therefore a need for monitoring much smaller areas in high tech building of today.

The development of stand alone microprocessor based controllers with communication facilities for VAV terminal units enabled the designers to provide monitoring of room conditions for the area served by each unit. A central micro-computer is used to handle the data from the 550 perimeter VAV terminals.

Figure 2 illustrates this arrangement.

## Figure 2

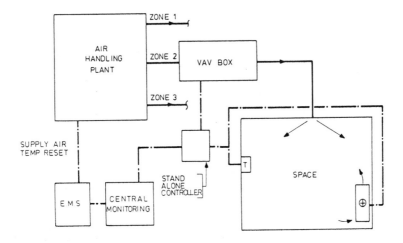

The final link in the feedback chain to the central plant was provided by a software interface package enabling the room temperature controllers to reset the respective zone supply air temperature such that as any terminal unit reaches it preset maximum cooling volume in response to room conditions, a signal is sent via the communication system to adjust down the zone supply air temperature. As the cooling demand subsequently drops so the appropriate supply air temperature is then reset up. In this way the most efficient supply air temperature/volume ratio can be controlled in the most energy efficient way.

The perimeter heating control is sequenced with the volume control on the terminal to avoid simultaneous heating and cooling.

Figure 3 indicates the feedback arrangement to the EMS.

Figure 3

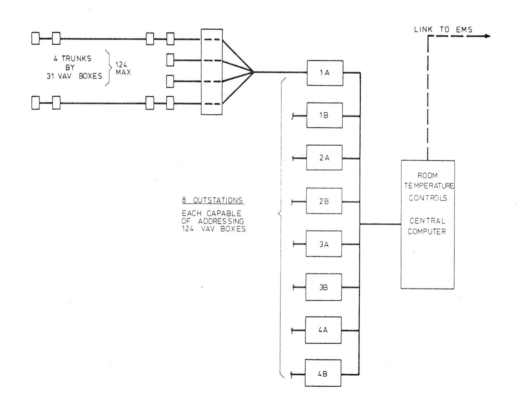

Having selected a system of central monitoring and control, other facilities are inherent within the system which provides benefits in the operation of the building. These include:

a. Room temperature set point adjustments for heating and cooling

b. VAV terminal maximum and minimum volume of adjustments

c. Room temperature indication

d. Supply air temperature indication

e. Velocity of supply air at terminal

f. High and low room temperature alarms

g. Global command facilities to control groups of terminals either on a system or location basis.

## 5. Maximising the Benefit of EMS

It is well known that one of the major difficulties experienced on many projects, particularly the larger, more complex ones, is achieving satisfactory completion which includes correct commissioning and performance testing, preparation of record documents and instruction to the Client's staff on operating the systems. Even if all of these items are completed to the satisfaction of all parties, in respect of contract requirements, this may not be adequate to ensure the most economical operation of the systems.

At best, it is likely that the systems will be commissioned to satisfy the bases of design. Generally, controls set points, for example, would be based upon theoretical steady state calculations, modified perhaps by the judgement of the commissioning engineer to reflect the dynamic response of the plant under the particular operating conditions obtaining at the time of the commissioning.

Using an EMS it is possible for the designer to fine tune the systems and controls to the building usage patterns and to the actual thermal response of the building elements and system components.

This activity is currently being undertaken by the authors utilising a direct BT Kilostream link installed between the EMS and a dynamic colour graphics VDU and printer modules in the design office. (See Figure 1). This will allow the engineers direct access to actual plant operating conditions and to the external climatic and internal conditions.

The activities undertaken by the engineers will include:

a. Monitoring energy use and energy cost

b. Development of energy audit procedures that will be the basis for future monitoring by the Client

c. Involving the Client's staff in monitoring procedures over an extended period in order for them to develop a full understanding of the installed systems

d. Checking the performance of the engineering systems using computer simulation techniques.

In this way the Client will gain the maximum benefit from a significant investment in the energy management system.

## 6. Linking EMS and Energy Simulation

For some years now the use of computer design methods for HVAC system sizing have been fairly common. These design programs are now being extended into the far more complex area of performance simulation. The aim of these new generation models is not only to simulate the performance of the building envelope but also the way in which the building with its engineering systems interact with climate and occupancy patterns experienced in a real situation.

One can see that with the increasing availability of relatively low cost but very powerful microprocessors, the EMS will eventually have an on-board simulation facility running in real time. This will have two major benefits. Firstly, it will significantly enhance the monitoring capability of the EMS in immediately being able to raise alarms if there is a significant departure from the design performance concept; the second area is in self learning adaptive control.

In order to start this technology moving forward into
this exciting new area, the authors, using the
Kilostream link already installed, will carry out energy
simulations using their in-house computering facilities.

Figure 4 illustrates this arrangement.

Figure 4

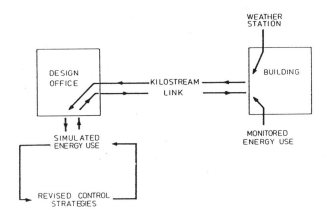

In order to check that the program is accurately
modelling the actual system performance, it will be
necessary for the simulation to be based upon the
climatic conditions obtaining at the time.  To this
end, a small meteorological station will be installed
on the roof of the building, linked to the EMS.  This
will monitor and record temperature , humidity, wind
speed and direction, and solar intensity.

The main objective of the simulation study is to
identify and investigate improvements to the systems
controls with a view to improving the overall energy
efficiency.  The system performance over a range of
different controls philosophies will be simulated
through a typical year's weather and operating
conditions.  It will be possible to carry out these
studies in a matter of hours.  Under normal plant
operating and monitoring procedures, this operation
would take many years to complete, even with the aid
of an EMS

In addition, the effect of changing requirements in the occupied spaces, perhaps due to an increase in cooling load from office equipment, could be simulated and an optimum controls strategy established before the change of use is made.

These simulation studies will enable the engineers to monitor the overall affect on energy consumption and advise the Client on control set points, plant switching times and the like to improve plant operating efficiency. Perhaps more important will be the ability to examine in detail a number of key factors relating to the overall controls strategy.

For example, it will be possible to examine the relationship between the variable air volume supply temperature and the volume flow rate under various operating conditions, and thus identify the optimum balance between the use of refrigeration energy and fan energy. Also, the spaces that have high levels of internal heat gain, and which would determine the supply air temperature for the whole zone would be identified, and where necessary, action taken to prevent a few extreme conditions adversely affecting overall energy use.

## 7. Summary

To achieve the full benefits of a comprehensive Energy Management System, it is not sufficient for designers to just be involved with its installation. The complexity of the systems for large high tech buildings requires a continued effort by skilled engineers to fine tune the system and controls. This period should also include the development of energy audit procedures and involvement of the Client's staff in order for them to gain a full understanding of the system's potential.

All too often complex systems are installed at great expense to the Client and their full benefits are never realised. The authors believe that a case can be made for the duties of the designer to be extended beyond contract completion to participate in the initial period of plant operation.

# Building management systems for retrofit

M D Clapp
Technical Director
Satchwell Control Systems Limited
England

80% of the buildings that will exist in 2050 are already built.
An existing building absorbs costs associated with both energy and
labour.  These costs include fuel charges, maintenance and
operational expenses and generally these costs will not be well
detailed and therefore will not be well managed or controlled.  The
paper sets out to show how modern Building Management Systems can be
retrofitted to such buildings with success.

Malcolm Clapp graduated in 1952 with a
degree in Electrical Engineering.  He
became a control engineer in the Weapons
Division of Fairey Aviation and later in
the Nuclear Division.
He joined Satchwell in 1968 to develop
electronic controls and management
systems, becoming Technical Director in
1979 responsible for all R & D and Quality
activities.
He has served on the IEE Energy Committee
and is currently a committee member of the
CIBSE Electrical Services Group.

Presented at HIGH-TECH BUILDINGS 87: Online Publications, Pinner, UK, 1987

## INTRODUCTION

80% of the buildings that will exist in 2050 are already built.

An existing building absorbs costs associated with both energy and labour.  These costs include fuel charges, maintenance and operational expenses and generally these costs will not be well detailed and therefore will not be well managed or controlled.

The application of a Building Management System achieves three objectives.  Firstly to monitor building conditions, failures and fuel usage.  Secondly to manage the maintenance function more efficiently and thirdly to control the various services.

This paper reviews the technology used in today's Building Management Systems and describes the use of intelligent remote outstations to obtain cost savings.  The importance of easy to use 'user friendly' systems which encourage the operators to take full advantage of the potential are noted with reference to Security and Fire Monitoring facilities.

Reference is made to Expert Systems and the prospective use of Building Management in the future.

Finally, several examples of Building Management Systems used in retrofit are described illustrating the various benefits obtained.

## RETROFIT

The term retrofit implies that the building is currently or has been operational and is now at a stage of refurbishment of fabric, fittings or services.

I shall confine my discussion to control of the services.  Changes to the fabric, improved insulation for example, can result in the plant becoming oversized and it is therefore important that any control system fitted or retrofitted can cope with this situation. It is an instance when self learning controls, that is controls which learn to adapt to the building and plant conditions, can be invaluable since manually resetting on a large site can be tedious and costly. (1)

In many existing buildings the HVAC valves and actuators are pneumatic as is the control system.  Modern electronics can give better and more flexible control and so an important element of controls retrofit is the facility to interface pneumatics with electronics.  This not only provides a better control system but significantly reduces the cost of the retrofit since valves and actuators can be left in place and no consequential drain down of the heating and cooling water circuit is necessary.

Another important aspect is the addition of secondary metering of energy use. The addition of meters to monitor heat, flow and electricity consumption will provide at an early stage knowledge of the site performance so important to produce the 'before and after' records.

Another generalisation is that controls in old buildings are not usually positioned for ease of monitoring. With modern BAS systems discrete controllers are unnecessary since the intelligent outstations can perform all the normal control functions with much less hardware. So when costing the retrofit it should be recognised that no replacement controls are required.

Considerable savings can be made by centralising the maintenance function since the BAS can perform conditions monitoring alerting the central maintenance function without requiring outside patrol inspection.

Modern BAS systems can monitor individual plant equipment efficiency and alarm limits can be set to alert maintenance of a fall off in performance which causes the running costs to rise previously unnoticed except by rising fuel bills after the event!

COMPUTER TECHNOLOGY

Following the invention of the transistor and integrated circuit techniques, rapid development took place in the digital computer field which was soon to have an impact on building control technology. The increase in computer capacity with reducing size and cost led to the emergence in the 1960's and early 1970's of the application of the computer to building management. (2)

Central Supervisory Systems were now designed around mini-computers, providing the system with the ability to calculate and make decisions arising from the information it received regarding environmental and plant conditions or status. The building supervisory system requiring man's intervention to make decisions about the management of the building became a building management system in its own right. Much less manual supervision was required, and the data handling capacity of the computer enabled many more data points and functions to be supervised and controlled than was previously possible.

The introduction of the computer into building management and control also enabled the first steps to be taken in the use of building management systems to economise in the use of energy in buildings. Optimisation of boilers and refrigeration plant, load shedding to reduce peak electricity demand and electric load cycling were among energy related programmes provided by such systems. Time sharing techniques enabled communication between the central computer console and its various remote outstations or data collection panels, to be achieved by simple twisted pair wiring, and remote buildings could be linked to the Central Management System via established telephone links.

Mini-computer based systems enjoyed significant growth during the early 1970's. However, although the cost per unit of computing power had reduced substantially, enabling in many instances a computer based system with much greater capacity, to be installed for no greater cost than previous non-computer based supervisory systems, the application of building management systems was limited by a number of features:-

*   The cost of the central mini-computer was not related to the actual amount of computer capacity required by a particular building. In many cases this meant that building management systems could not be cost effective.

*   Over enthusiasm by designers and the desire to justify the computer by making full use of its capacity, led sometimes to over elaborate systems which were not fully or properly used in practice, and a consequential adverse effect on their reputation.

*   The lack of computer operating experience on the part of building engineers often led to under utilisation of the system - the engineer is reluctant to use equipment which he does not understand or feel "in control of".

So, in general the application of computer technology has tended to be limited by cost and other factors to very large buildings. Recent technological developments are already changing this situation.

## TOTAL BUILDING AUTOMATION/MANAGEMENT SYSTEMS

The use of microprocessor technology in Building Automation/ Management Systems is rapidly superseding the central mini-computer. There are a number of significant advantages:-

*   The total computing power of the system no longer needs to be concentrated at the central console. That part of the system intelligence required to carry out monitoring and local control functions for remote plant rooms and equipment, can now be located within the outstations or data receiving panels located adjacent to the plant they supervise. Thus, remote outstations, previously non-intelligent sub-panels, whose function was limited to receipt and transmission of data to and from the central console, become local control stations, capable of carrying out complex control functions. Communication with the central console being necessary only when commands are being issued from

the centre, or when information available or stored at the outstation is required at the central location or abnormal conditions occur which must be reported.  The reduction of computing power necessary at the central console renders a conventional mini-computer unnecessary.  Consequently, while the cost of the now intelligent outstations increases, the total cost of the building management system is more directly related to the actual computing requirements of the building.  Reduced data rates resulting from distribution of the decision making process into outstations, leads to lower cost inter-connection and more reliable communications.  Thus using microprocessor technology and the distributed intelligence design approach, comprehensive building management systems can be cost justified for much smaller buildings.

*   The intelligent remote outstation, once programmed from the central console, can be designed to possess full local control integrity, such that it will continue to operate its local plant functions as programmed in spite of any failure of the communications link with the central console or of the central console itself.  This is a substantial advance on central mini-computer systems where failure of the central computer rendered the total system inoperative.

*   The computing capacity available allows the use of higher level programming languages.  Interactive user programming of the system using a question and answer "prompting" technique, simplifies the operator's task.  The operator no longer needs to understand computers in order to use the system; he can communicate with the system in his own language without the use of elaborate codes.

*   The distribution of system intelligence into remote outstations, and the design of software in modular form greatly increases the degree of choice which can be exercised by the potential user, in selecting programmes and facilities to match the system to the needs of his particular building. (3)

In addition, the initial system can be easily expanded at a later date to include additional facilities without expensive alteration to the system initially installed.

The control facilities available with modern distributed intelligence microprocessor based building management systems, include:-

Plant Alarm and Status Monitoring and Logging.

Optimisation of Boiler and Refrigeration Plant Operation.

Optimum Start/Stop of Heating and Cooling Plant.

Security and Fire Alarm System Monitoring.

Plant Maintenance Scheduling.

Control of Remote Buildings via Telephone Link.

Energy Consumption Logging.

Electrical Load Cycling and Maximum Demand Control.

Electric Lighting Control.

Because the computing power necessary to achieve these functions can now be provided at lower cost, the potential market for sophisticated building management systems is no longer limited only to very large buildings. (4)

COST SAVINGS

Cost savings arising from the more efficient use of fuel and manpower have been achieved by the use of Building Management and Control Systems throughout the industrialised world. Fuel savings come mainly from the elimination of wasteful use at non-occupied times and the control of the maximum demand tariff on electrically supplied systems. (5)

The more effective and efficient use of manpower for managing and maintaining building services enables building owners to employ Energy Managers with specific knowledge of the systems employed in a modern building as well as the less energy efficient earlier buildings.

The use of the latest low cost microprocessor and electronic techniques can aid the Energy Manager to have a much more thorough understanding of the performance of his building.

It is important that the data produced and the method of using the equipment is simple and user friendly.

Examples of 1-3 years payback are shown in Table 1. The results are those obtained using a microprocessor based Distributed Intelligence Building Management System.

Table 1 - Sample Case History

|  | CASE 1 | CASE 2 | CASE 3 | CASE 4 |
|---|---|---|---|---|
| Type of Site | Hospital | Industrial | Industrial | University |
| Investment | 30,000 | 25,000 | 114,000 | 50,000 |
| Savings/Year (£) | 20,000 | 26,000 | 37,000 | 25,000 |
| Payback Period | 1½ Years | 1 Year | 3 Years | 2 Years |

## BUSINESS INFORMATION

During the past few years much interest has developed in the integration of energy management data into the total management of a building.  The transfer of data from the BMS to the computers is now taking place.  This requires the BMS manufacturer to provide a standard output port RS-232, -422, -423 or similar and define the memory locations in which the data may be found together with the message structure for the other computer to 'talk to' the BMS.  An example developed by the DHSS is the Works Information Management System, WIMS.  Information such as status and trend logs as well as totalised hours run and meter readings are normally transferred.

Another application that the Building Management System has been put to is the monitoring of production machinery.  Here hours run and breakdown information can be gathered centrally via intelligent outstations thus providing a valuable tool to Works Management.

## USER FRIENDLY TECHNIQUES

To maximise the cost savings possible from managing the services in a building, diagnostic techniques to determine and alarm abnormal and inefficient situations must be used.  This data must be directed to the relevant division of building services.  For example, Fire, Security, Maintenance alarms should be routed separately to where they can be dealt with most effectively.

The message content must be explicit and easy to understand including the maintenance instructions, part numbers for spares and fitting details.

The system has become a 'Knowledge based expert system'.

Failure to keep it simple will result in the operator disregarding and not using the system.  Many of the earlier systems now lay neglected and unused because they required interpretation of codes to analyse alarms, lists of logged readings instead of identified trend graphs and above all, they needed programmers to alter conditions in the system.

Today menu driven systems lead the operator by the hand and the man/machine combination has become very powerful.

## SECURITY SYSTEMS

As the gap between the 'haves' and 'have nots' widens the former become more concerned with retaining their possessions.  Whilst the latter employ the advancing technology to assist in their illegal pursuits.

Security is now concerned with protecting people, goods and materials, and the latest focus of attention, the computer with its data and instant credit transfer facility.

Let us look at each of these areas in turn.

Some people need to be kept out of certain areas, the high security buildings and sites, whilst other people need to be traced and locatable within an area.  In the first instance areas are protected with fences, check points and locked access gates and doors. Surveillance systems employing Doppler devices and Sonic standing wave patterns have superseded the more mature light beams and electric fences.  Microprocessors play an important role in this developing 'high tech' security business.

Access control now no longer needs the rather inconvenient key or card to be physically inserted in a reader at the entrance.  After all these can be stolen and fairly easily duplicated.  One is reminded of the burglar with the bar of soap as a tool of the trade to make key impressions.

No, today's access systems can be much more secure and difficult to evade.  Intelligent tags are now available which actively respond electromagnetically to automatic computer controlled outstations to allow door control without effort from the would be entrant.  When combined with voice print detection, since each of us has a unique natural pattern, it gives a very secure system.

In the second situation people need to be traced within a site or building.  Such examples are security guards, doctors, service engineers.  The traditional radio paging device has advanced in the past year or so now being capable of delivering displayed messages on an LCD panel incorporated in the device where a microprocessor decodes the received message.  Such pagers can operate Nationwide using the Air Call Service.  Building Management Systems can provide the guard patrol routines which track security guards around a site. These employ time measurement between check points as well as voice print and tag identification.

In the early days of access control where the reader was connected back to a central location embarrassing delays were experienced as each person entered the access control point.  Now intelligent outstations make the decisions.

Locating Service Engineers on a large site can be frustrating. Modern techniques can be used to produce an identified light spot on the graphics display system in a manner similar to that used by air traffic control radars.  The recent press reports of 'Hackers' breaking into private computer files gives an example of how technology can be used for evil as well as for making for business efficiency.  A combination of voice print and security codes would make this modern felony less likely.

## FIRE MONITORING

The immense computing power of the microprocessor has not as yet been allowed to make the contribution to fire control that it could. Most Building Management Systems connect into the fire alarm system using 'volt free' contacts and the BMS simply acts as an enhanced repeater showing alarms on the dynamic graphics screen and printing out at the fire monitoring station.

Using temperature sensors together with an algorithm to calculate rate of rise, the centre and direction of travel of the fire is possible with the benefit of greatly assisting evacuation and consequential life saving.

## EXPERT SYSTEMS

One of the most exciting developments which will impact on Building Automation over the next decade will be the use of Expert Systems. (6)

Expert Systems make use of Artificial Intelligence and are concerned with making machines carry out tasks which, were they performed by humans, would be considered to require intelligence.

Considerable investment is taking place throughout the world on the development of Artificial Intelligence, Expert Systems, Knowledge Based Systems and Super Computers.  (7)

Knowledge Based Systems use human experience in order to draw conclusions from a set of conditions.  Their process units use IF --- AND --- THEN --- statements to arrive at a conclusion.

Further refinement will be achieved by the introduction of experience from past exercises.  For example:

If X and Y and Z then conclusion is P or Q.

From past experience with the same conditions the probability of P is 0.8 and that of Q = 0.3.

Then the probable conclusion is P and associated with each number is a certainty factor.

It is important that all experience is added to the data base to refine the deductive process.

Within the context of Building Management it is certain that decisions based on information supplied by BMS are being ignored or overlooked, leaving the full implication of the data gathering opportunities to be unrealised. Clearly the use of an Expert System would provide assistance in interpreting the considerable volume of information available from the sensors to the BMS.

Expert systems need to be developed to assist in the design and use of automated building services.

## NETWORKS

The trend towards distributed computing has accelerated the development of networked systems. These systems provide for the linking of equipments ranging from meters, sensors and controllers to Visual Display Terminals and Printers. The link up can occur in a building or small site using Local Area Networks (LANS) over multiple buildings such as an Industrial Estate using Metropolitan Area Networks (MANS) and Nationwide or even Internationally using Wide Area Networks (WANS) which make use of the Public Switched Telephone Network (PSTN) or radio communication.

As Networks become bigger it will become necessary to interconnect equipments from different manufacturers and so there is a need to standardise the communications protocol whilst still allowing individual manufacturers to display innovation so often stifled by standardisation. (8)

## MICROWAVE LINKS

British Gas North Western (BGNW) have used their own microwave links to control the gas transmission system for more than 25 years. They are now installing a new digital microwave network to link up their Building Management Systems.

North Western is the largest Region of British Gas with over 2.2 million customers and sales exceeding 2000 million therms a year. (9)

It covers 3900 square miles including the counties of Greater Manchester, Merseyside, Lancashire and Cheshire and parts of Cumbria, Derbyshire, Shropshire and North Yorkshire.

In 1977 and 1981 the Region won the Gas Energy Management award. The award is presented annually by British Gas to the partnership of Industrialist and Gas Region which jointly is judged to have made the most significant contribution to the efficient use of gas and therefore towards energy conservation.

In 1981 BGNW commenced installing BAS 700 Building Management
Systems at their Operational Control Centres providing control of
chillers and boilers as well as lighting and pump and fan
sequencing. The resultant savings were impressive, in excess of 40%
saved.

The BASNET will link up the Region's BAS 700 Building Management
Systems and relay information back to Welman House, BGNW
Headquarters.

There are three main legs, each headed by a new Operational Control
Centre which communicates with all other sites on the leg.

The Property Department at Welman House will have a BAS terminal,
colour graphics and printers allowing information and alarms to be
received from anywhere on the network.

RETROFIT IN THE STORE

Harrods of Knightsbridge was built some 90 years ago and the
building occupies a 4½ acre site and has some 63,000 square metres
of sales floors with 230 separate departments, serving an average of
50,000 customers each day.

The annual energy cost is £2 million and the plant includes 5 main
oil fired steam boilers plus hot water boilers. There are 140
separate air handling units plus chillers and cooling towers.

Below the store is a main electricity generating plant which enables
Harrods to produce 60% of the electrical load if required.

It also has its own artesian well with pumping sets.

The installation of a BAS 700 Building Management System provides
the engineering, maintenance and stores staff with an effective and
centralised means of monitoring the numerous areas and plant rooms
much more effectively than had been previously possible.

The first phase includes 10 outstations and has concentrated on
monitoring the main boiler and electrical generating plants. Remote
meter reading of oil tank contents and electricity usage has also
been included.

The second phase will bring under automatic control the air
distribution system which has been manually adjusted in the past.

The use of intelligent standalone outstations capable of monitoring
and controlling and yet communicating information and alarms to a
central area makes the online expansion of such a system possible.

## FUTURE TRENDS

The use of standalone outstations with significant computer power allows buildings widely spread geographically to be networked to a headquarters building or to a maintenance company who will undertake total maintenance of clients buildings. Some contracts are arranged on a lease/hire basis where the client pays an annual payment for the maintenance organisation to manage his services. Some see this as an attraction since no capital purchase has to be justified. But as seen in Table 1, a payback in 3 years is still a viable investment.

The present day outstations are very powerful and can incorporate fire alarm and security services including access control.

Another future trend will be to use the BMS to monitor industrial machines for malfunction, quality of output, operation condition (running, set up, maintenance).

The data collection ability is a vital input to the Business Management System and associated computer.

The growing interest in Direct Digital Control (DDC) has been overtaken by DDDC, Distributed Direct Digital Control where the outstations can run PID algorithms independently of each other thus giving the total system a greater reliability.

## CONCLUSIONS

"To be efficient you must know what is happening and having determined what is happening you have to be able to exercise some control over events. Good sources of information are therefore essential." (9)

Effective control undoubtedly provides the biggest pay back in terms of energy conservation and reduced running costs.

This paper has illustrated some case studies of retrofitting existing buildings and building complexes. Retrofit will continue to be the major focus for improvement in running costs since the capital cost of new building and the relative scarcity of suitable building sites will dictate this approach.

There are many inefficient buildings not necessarily because they are bad buildings but because maintenance and management of them is difficult and has been allowed to lapse. Modern Building Management Systems are established and have a proven track record of being able to provide expert assistance to those who are charged with the management of the buildings of yesterday and tomorrow.

REFERENCES

(1) Clapp, M.D. - "Automatic Controls - Design and Performance Criterea". Proceedings of Symposium Automatic Controls for Building Services - Why and How - CIBS, March 1978.

(2) Murrell, A.S., Clapp, M.D. - Markets for New or Advanced Building Controls Technologies or Equipments. I.E.A. Conference, Berlin, 1981.

(3) Clapp, M.D. - Automation for Energy Management. B.I.M. Conference, London, October 1979.

(4) Clapp, M.D. - "Monitoring and Control Using Energy Management Systems". IEE - Colloquium Resource, Conservation and the Electrical Engineer Digest No. 1983/62 - April 1983.

(5) Clapp, M.D. - "Cost Savings Using Building Management and Control Systems" - Proceedings Clima 2000, Copenhagen 1985.

(6) Turner, M. - Expert Systems: A Management Guide, PA Computers and Telecommunications 1984.

(7) Hamilton, G. and Harrison, A. - Expert Systems for the Construction and Building Services Industry - Technical Note TN 7/86, BSRIA.

(8) Birtles, A.B. - Building Management Systems - Objective Appraisal. Proceedings of CICC Conference "Energy Management in Buildings", Nottingham, March 1984.

(9) Taylor, C.H. and Evans, P.W. - British Gas North Western "Building for Efficiency" paper to Institution of Gas Engineers. September 1986.

# Responsive energy management systems: the practical approach to total integration

JOHN E. LAWRENCE, M.B.E.
Chairman & Managing Director
JEL Energy Conservation Services Limited
England

The demand for integration of building services including environmental control, energy efficiency, fire, security and access systems is the practical approach to servicing the users' needs of the future.

This paper investigates the boundaries of possibilities and how it can be achieved technically, accepting that there are many companies specialising in different sectors. The technology exists for more integration to cover all the services needed in a building, but one would question the need for relying upon one micro-processor electronic controller to bring together all the different facets. Options exist and these should be explored, benefits and pitfalls.

John E. Lawrence, M.B.E. is Chairman & Managing Director of JEL, a company he formed in 1974, which specialises in electronic controls and energy management systems. In February 1984, Mr. Lawrence was appointed one of five Marketing Advisors to the Secretary of State for Energy, and was awarded the M.B.E. in the Queen's Birthday Honours List in May 1984.

Presented at HIGH-TECH BUILDINGS 87: Online Publications, Pinner, UK, 1987

## Introduction

Integration in high tech or the so-called intelligent buildings can be interpreted in many ways dependent upon where your particular interest lies, and at any moment in time. It is, however, true that there is a positive market demand for engineers to attempt to piece together the three key issues :

Total Building Services

The electronic infra-structure of the building

The information processes

From my viewpoint, it is highly unlikely that this will be achieved within a 5-10 year period, however desirable some people may think it is.

The high tech building could be described as one which integrates various systems to effectively manage resources in a co-ordinated mode to maximise :-

Occupant performance

Investment and operating cost savings

Flexibility

This paper examines the practical approach to total integration using the energy and building management system as the core activity, bringing together all the building services before taking the next major step forward – the fully integrated data highway management of all the systems.

The unfortunate situation in the U.K. is that it takes too long to get our act together and decide, in the best interest of all groups, what the standards will be to allow our manufacturers and applicators to get on with the job.

However, a lot of work has been going on behind the scenes in the different market disciplines, but if integration is to be successfully accepted, then one's own market niche depends on others agreeing to talk to each other. It is recognised that the Building Energy Management Systems business is getting its act together with the recent formation of the BEMS Centre in which major U.K. manufacturers of control systems are now talking about standards and compatibility at high level.  This is an excellent step forward, supported financially by the Department of Energy, users and other interest groups.

## Today's Technology, EMS – BMS

Electronic energy management systems (EMS) are only one aspect related to the management of services in today's buildings.  They relate generally to the automatic control of the environment, encompassing discpline over such things as lighting; heating; ventilation; air conditioning; refrigeration and electrical load in order to improve performance and hence run plant efficiently. It is the control system that makes energy costs controllable.

Historically, the control of the services in a building was done by discreet stand-alone controls, but with technology changes, particularly in electronics, more capability and intelligence has meant more of the building services can be integrated.  There has been greater innovative use of the microprocessor and software which has led to owners, designers and engineers understanding what is practical and valuable in day-to-day use.

If one examined the functions of a Building Management System (BMS), we would expect it to typically support the following :

* Automatically control the mechanical and electrical plant to maintain required conditions and operate it efficiently

* Be capable of mimicking and where possible and appropriate, fire/security, access, lifts, etc.

* Monitor the building performance quickly, efficiently and reliably, automatically alarming problem areas.  Allowing prompt support and corrective action when things go wrong

* Provide detailed up-to-the-minute information on a computer screen as to what the current situation is of any plant however complex, throughout the building

* Provide a basis for historical performance
data to be archived and used for future
comparison and enable maintenance effectiveness
to be improved

* Provide valuable information to the
designers of buildings and services
giving positive feedback for future use

Controls systems managing the environment have changed
dramatically over the last ten years from discreet analogue
devices handling a single loop or function, to Direct Digital
Control (D.D.C.). The D.D.C. outstations control and monitor
multiple loops and handle communications between each other
and the central computer even over telephone lines where
appropriate.

With the advent of more powerful microprocessors and a new
generation of software and improved communication systems, it
is easy to understand why so many people in our engineering
professions are using these systems to improve performance and
reduce energy costs by between 10 and 20%.

In an EMS or BMS system, the central computer can be looked
upon as a Managing Director of a company. It dictates, master-
minds and controls what is going on in the building – it is
capable of being informed when something is wrong and then
issuing new commands, and corrective actions to secure better
overall efficiency and management of the building.

The stand–alone outstations can be referred to as the line
managers – getting on with their tasks without reference, until
they have a decision superimposed from central or one of their
colleagues alongside.

Bringing the different facets together

If we had to manage the operation of all the building services
and collect all the data in a meaningful and useful format with
one single computer, then we have to accept the existence of
rules, regulations and self–interest groups, pulling against the
use of standard communications systems.

We can currently say there are very few energy/building management systems which have a truly integrated capability that would allow ISDN or other network connection. So the first step must be to bring together the capability to electronically communicate on to a common highway and address the different facets, with products manufactured by different companies.

Environmental control (HEVAC)

Lighting

Load Management

Fire and Security

Access Control

Lift/Elevator Control

Current legislation dictates that the FIRE system should be separate in hardware terms to that of, for example, a lighting or temperature control system, and for insurance purposes, a SECURITY system is purchased separately to that of the energy management scheme, and the same could be said in some instances with regard to Access Control and C.C.T.V.

If one looks at Lifts and Elevators, rarely is this integrated into the building management system, but yet it is one of the most complex control functions in a building.

Lift management is a complimentary operation to other building management services and is operated by the same personnel, although maintenance is often entirely delegated to the lift manufacturer. Lift management is the long term process by which the operation of all the lifts in say a number of groups can be controlled and optimised and maintained at peak performance, and there must be sufficient flexibility such that the control of the lifts can be tailored to the changing needs of the building. Without this management control, the occupants must tailor their requirements to the services provided by the lifts.

The common path for the future is to ensure that all these different facets are microprocessor controlled with communication capability, possibly through a standard node which allows communications to a local area network. Control and monitoring from one or more CPU's and printers and other peripheral items is then possible.

See Appendix I.

Once the key issues of standard protocol and communication have been addressed in the building energy management systems business, and there are options available for users to select different modules relative to their application needs, then the management and maintenance of buildings will improve significantly.

If one uses the building services sector as a model with extreme complexity, managing the operation of many different pieces of plant and equipment, then I am sure integration in the process industry, office automation and information systems will be achieved with time.

## Appendix I

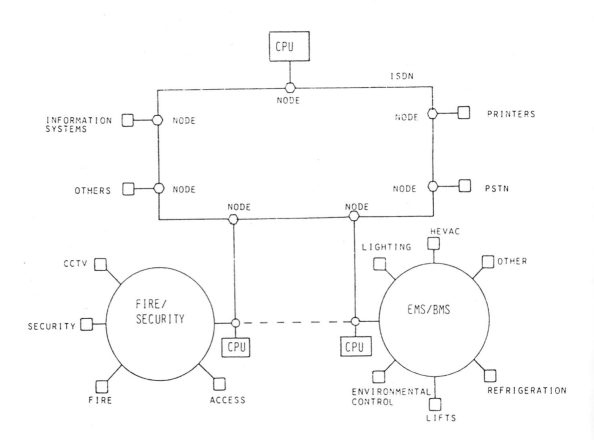

# Integration of fire & security with energy management

J.David Walter
Business Marketing Manager
Thorn Security Limited
UK

Integration of fire and security systems with energy
management has now become the preferred solution for larger
buildings.  There are many benefits for the system
specifier, owner and end user however the three disciplines
differ in their requirements for the electronics, standards
and industry codes of practice.

David Walter is currently Business Marketing
Manager for Thorn Security which has recently
changed its name from THORN EMI PROTECH.
David joined Thorn from Chubb Fire in 1985
where he was Product Manager for fire
detection, systems.  He is now responsible
for marketing his company's range of fire,
security and energy management systems and
services.

Presented at HIGH-TECH BUILDINGS 87: Online Publications, Pinner, UK, 1987

## Introduction

The user of virtually any existing building can choose to instal High-Tech systems. His choice of system will depend upon his present and predicted needs and his motive will invariably be the safe, efficient and profitable operation of his business.

When we talk about High Tech buildings we generally mean buildings designed as an entity, a complete system with all parts working in harmony to provide a comfortable, efficient and safe environment. We can draw an analogy with the human body where virtually every part is a highly desirable, if not an essential, part of the whole. However, just as the legs of an Olympic runner are not needed by an average typist - high speed data communications is not required by a diamond merchant. Since the needs of users and the users themselves will often change during the life of the building the systems incorporated within the infrastructure must themselves be capable of being adapted to meet changing requirements.

It could be argued that all of the components and systems comprising even the simplest Low-Tech building are already "integrated"; the light switch is close to the door, a timeswitch turns the heating on in the morning, the PA microphone is close to the switchboard which is in reception; generally everything is chosen and installed to make life easy. The issue facing this conference is how we can make buildings more efficient, comfortable, profitable and safe using modern technology to best effect.

This paper deals with the integration of building systems, particularly the integration of fire with security and energy management. The need for an integrated approach, a flexible system, the differing constraints on the electronics required for different disciplines, and the need for ongoing service and maintenance, are among the issues discussed.

In the context of High Tech buildings 'fire' is taken to mean automatic fire detection and alarm systems. 'Security' is taken to mean electronic security systems such as intruder alarms, access control, closed circuit television, perimeter protection etc.

## So why integrate?

Like the human body all of the components of a building are
present together to make the whole.  It is technically
possible to provide electronic connections between any
building services but I suggest that it is no more logical
to integrate the telephone system with the energy management
system than it would be, say, to integrate your tongue with
your big toe.  Both have totally different functions and the
condition in one is never dependent upon the condition in
the other.  Fire, security and energy management systems,
however, share a crucial factor - they all need to be
monitored for alarm and fault conditions.  In addition, when
more than one alarm is received at a time, it is important
that the correct priority is placed on each.  In small
buildings multiple alarms are a very rare occurence but as
buildings get larger and the number of detectors increase
then the probability of multiple alarms rises considerably,
particularly in an emergency.  By integrating fire, security
and energy management functions into one central
display/control computer the operator (who is often
unskilled) can be presented with required actions in the
correct sequence according to predetermined priority.

In addition the entire system can be controlled, monitored
and faults diagnosed by the skilled operator or service
engineer from one central point.  This permits faster and
more efficient maintenance and reduces nuisance to the
user.

The latest systems are capable of detecting and indicating
incipient faults within their own components so the service
engineer can be called before the system actually
malfunctions and told in advance which spare parts he should
bring with him.

Suppliers can offer regular maintenance (invariably required
for fire and security systems) at more attractive rates for
integrated systems because only one call is required.
Because the latest systems can accurately record all alarms,
faults and actions, troublesome areas can be quickly
identified and problems resolved before the user suffers
undue nuisance.

The flexible nature of an integrated fire/security and
energy management system permits changes to be made as the
needs or users change.  Often all that is required is a
minor change to the configuration of software in the central
computer - which can normally be performed on site.

In the case of multi-tenanted buildings, sophisticated services (e.g. access control) can often be offered at lower cost than would be possible using stand-alone systems and the invoicing of energy used becomes possible.

## How should systems be integrated?

With the introduction of less expensive, smaller and yet more powerful microcomputers the trend throughout industry is to distribute intelligence further and further into the field, away from the central computer. The advantage of this approach is that sub systems may be autonomous and can continue to function correctly even with major failures in other parts of the system. (Here the analogy with the human body is stretched to breaking point - what would be the use of an autonomous foot?) There is now and there will always be, a far greater market for small stand-alone systems than for large integrated systems; thousands of products are being installed daily by dozens of suppliers in every conceivable application. These products are highly reliable since they have been designed in the light of a wealth of field experience and new products are quickly 'debugged' because of the numbers installed. It is wise, therefore, to select components for the integrated system from standard product ranges.

This is consistent with the "distributed intelligence" philosophy and the user is assured of sub systems which have been designed and fully proven for stand-alone use. Servicing is simpler since the supplier's engineers will undoubtedly be more expert with those products they use most often and spares are likely to be more readily available.

The system should consist, therefore, of a number of standard products designed to be interfaced to one another, connected to a central computer with a control and display facility. Whilst the precise tailoring or 'configuration' of the central software will vary from building to building, experience has shown that the best results are achieved by using standard computer hardware and a standard core software package capable of being configured on site.

More than one console may be fitted to the system, for
example there may be a need for displays in guard rooms,
reception, financial services etc. The requirements for
each of these consoles may be different and often the degree
of control from any console will need to change either
according to the time of day or change of shift. Therefore
the system should be flexible enough to permit a wide range
of operating modes which can be easily changed by the user.

## Electronics for the Different Disciplines

The two main differences between the electronic requirements
for the three disciplines are

    a)    Data Communication

    b)    Integrity

In an energy mangement system large numbers of accurate
analogue signals need to be constantly transmitted from
sensors to local control panels and from the panels to
valves. The communications path is, therefore, very busy.
In a security system a smaller number of random digital
events need to be transmitted to the local controller (which
is normally programmed to ignore these signals during normal
working hours). In a fire system it is hoped that few, if
any, signals are sent from the detector to the local
controller (although some of the more modern detectors now
constantly transmit analogue levels representing perceived
smoke, heat etc. to the local controller).

In terms of the integrity required for the different systems
it is unlikely that any deliberate attempt will be made to
interfere with energy management or fire systems (other then
crude vandalism) whereas a security system is a target for
the criminal genius.

Integrated systems should be designed to withstand the worst
conditions of each discipline. For example a system
designed primarily for energy management whilst perfectly
able to transmit security alarms may not incorporate the
necessary safeguards to thwart the criminal.

## Standards

In Britain there are no regulatory authorities covering
energy management or security systems although when intruder
alarms are required for insurance purposes the insurer will
invariably insist upon a supplier who is a member of the
National Supervisory Council for Intruder Alarms (NSCIA).
Nearly all security systems installed in Britain are either
at the express request of an insurance company or to obtain
a reduction in insurance premium therefore the majority of
security companies are members of the NSCIA and can supply
NSCIA certificates which declare that the system has been
installed in accordance with the recognised Code of
Practice.

In Britain the regulatory authorities for fire systems are

> Fire Offices Committee (FOC)
> Fire Officers (FOs)

The FOC which has recently become a part of the Loss
Prevention Council (LPC) is mainly concerned with fire
detection and extinguishing systems for insurance purposes.
Although FOC certificates are issued by an FOC approved
supplier rather than the FOC themselves, the supplier may
only instal components which have been approved and tested
for use in a specific system.  The fact that all components
of a system may have FOC approval does not mean that the
system will qualify for an FOC certificate.  Most
manufacturers submit their products to a test house (at
their own expense) and request approval for their products
to be combined to make a range of systems.

With regard to integrated systems the FOC (or the LPC as
they should be more correctly called) are perfectly happy to
accept integration with other disciplines provided that no
defect in the other systems could possibly result in a fault
in the fire system.  In addition they require that the
'alarm path' is an approved system and this includes all
components from fire detectors through to bells and
signalling equipment.

Fire Officers, on the other hand, are only concerned with
the safety of the building.  FOs consider all fire safety
matters such as evacuation routes, emergency lighting, exit
signs, adequate alarms etc.  The FO issues the Fire
Certificate which is required before a building is
occupied.

## Benefits of Integration

From the specifier and client's point of view, it is far
simpler to deal with one supplier who can be contractually
held to provide a complete working system.   In addition only
one call needs to be made in case of malfunction - and there
are no arguments over whose equipment is defective or whose
responsibility it is.

Another important benefit to the user is that all alarm
information can be presented on a single console in a clear,
unambiguous format.   The philosophical debate regarding
correct action in the case of different emergencies can all
take place before the building is even occupied; even an
unskilled operator only has to cope with one or two simple
instructions at a time.   The skilled operator, on the other
hand, can get a far better picture of the situation within
the building with an integrated system and can control
events more effectively and more safely.

The techniques on integration need not be limited to one
building.   A number of buildings can be networked either
over the public telephone network or over a private network
to provide a total control and monitoring facility at one
location.   Groups of buildings such as university campuses,
hospitals and local schools can all benefit from central
monitoring and a number of schemes are already successfully
in operation.

Selection of the best products is only half the story.   Not
only do they have to be engineered as a system (which needs
a truly multidiscipline engineering capability) the system
will need to be maintained over many years (which means a
truly multidiscipline service capability).   Unfortunately
this point is sometimes overlooked and has led to a number
of expensive mistakes.

## Conclusion

Integration of fire security and energy management systems
can offer very real benefits and is now the preferred
solution for larger buildings.

# Untangling the entanglement

David Firnberg
Managing Director, Eosys Limited: and
Chairman, The Networking Centre

Few organisations are aware how important the wiring in
their building is to them, and how vulnerable they are
to a wiring failure.

There are many different cables needed in todays offices.
The obvious ones are the data and voice cables linking
the workstations and the telephones to each other, to
some central resource, and to the outside world.

Hidden away however, there are many other cables which
are involved with the environment. Lighting, heating and
ventilation; access control, surveillance and security;
earthing and lightning conductors. These all require some
form of signal cabling. And of course, there are the power
cables distributing electricity to wherever it is needed.

Based on substantial case studies, the Eosys Cable
Management Programme brought together all aspects of
Cable Management in order to provide practical tools and
guidelines for the planning and management of all types
of cable systems throughout their life cycle.

Eosys has undertaken cabling assignments for many
organisations ranging from wiring up Grade I listed
buildings or planning refurbishments prior to an office
move, to comprehensive arrangements for brand new buildings.

DAVID FIRNBERG is Managing Director
of Eosys, the information technology
consultancy. He is also Chairman
of The Networking Centre based in
Hemel Hempstead which tests products
for conformance to the OSI standards,
including MAP/TOP.

A past president of the British
Computer Society and from 1975-80
the Director of the National Computing
Centre (NCC), David Firnberg has been
in the forefront of the practical
application of information technology
for over 30 years.

Presented at HIGH-TECH BUILDINGS 87: Online Publications, Pinner, UK, 1987

## Cables Matter

Cables are the arteries and nerves which give life to a building and the operations that take place within it. The failure of a data or power cable can have catastrophic effects on day to day operations and yet the planning, management, maintenance and control of cabling is often completely ignored.

Throughout industry, but particularly in commercial offices, there has been a period of messy and expensive mistakes in the selection and use of information technology (IT) equipment. This, of course, is bad news for the organisational budget - but it is visible: it shows. And so it is put right.

The cables that service those wrongly selected pieces of equipment are as deeply implicated in that expensive period of over-enthusiasm. But they aren't visible. Very often, as we found in our research, they don't even show in the correct account books. And so they remain, uncosted - and the victim of overwhelmingly ad hoc solutions to perfectly analysable problems. The aim of the Eosys Cable Management Programme was to point out that there is a cabling problem, that it is susceptible to a management programme, and that failure to implement such a programme will inevitably carry serious cost implications.

## Who is Responsible?

IT equipment is dependent upon power and communication links but because of the disproportionate importance of the equipment, which is much more expensive than the equally vital cabling, and has a much shorter life cycle this dependence is frequently ignored. Once the cabling is installed it is forgotten, while the high profile equipment continues to attract attention.

There is a temptation to treat all electronic problems as equipment problems, when it may well be that the fault lies buried somewhere in the cabling. In addition, cabling affects the whole building and buildings can become obsolete; one of the ways in which they show their obsolescence is their inability to deal with cable.

Normally no one person is responsible for cabling, rather responsibility is split three ways.  Power, telecoms and data cabling allocated to building services, the communications and computing respectively. Further, different sets of people may be responsible at the various stages of specifying, procuring, installing, maintaining and reconfiguring cable systems.

## Cabling - A Poor Relation

At every stage, cabling is seen - if it is seen at all - as the poor relation.

- Architects make no, or very little, provision for cable, and frequently neglect the all important interface between vertical and horizontal planes of distribution.

- Economics seem to have passed cabling by - very few organisations know how much their cables cost, let alone the value of the information they carry.

- Users' awareness is, generally, lamentable - but no less lamentable than suppliers' lack of awareness of the needs of users.

- Installers called in to deal with the expensive new acquisitions may have no experience of data or telecoms cabling, and may treat and test all cabling as power.

- The regulations are designed, very properly, with safety in mind - but the result is that all suppliers want their own trunking.  Add together IBM, Wang, BT, Mercury, the PABX and power - you have six-compartment trunking and perhaps six separate earths.

Against this background of a low priority for cable, there is the unstemmable movement in technology towards greater integration - such as voice and data - which may indeed result in less cable but will certainly produce

infinitely more complex electronic relationships,
dependent on cables.  And this in an information climate
in which the importance of earthing, noise on cable and
lightning protection are still not fully appreciated.


## Planes of Distribution

The Eosys approach to cable management has been to hold
to the concept of networks - power, data, telecoms - and
to regard these networks as existing on one or more of
three planes of distribution.


Primary cable ascends through risers and core ducts from
main incoming supply points or from on-floor equipment
to each floor of the building.


Secondary cabling moves through the horizontal plane of
the building - that is, across each floor in the plane
of the floor, wall or ceiling.  Tertiary cabling emerges
from the building scenery elements - floor, wall or
ceiling - to be distributed to and between items of
equipment.


The difference is largely one of degrees of freedom.
The first is tightly constrained by the building riser -
one spatial dimension.  The second is free to rotate
around the point where it emerges from the riser.  The
third is free to move in the three dimensions of space.


These differences present quite distinct management and
design problems.  But the three levels and their
problems must be confronted simultaneously - performance
at one level cannot be bought at the expense of lack of
capacity at another.


## Applications

Nor is it just a question of three networks, rather
there are three types of network, power, data and
telecom, serving eight groups of applications.  These
are:

- data and message communications both to end users and computer to computer

- voice communications for telephones, answering machines, and voice messaging systems

- image communications, CCTV for security for example

- building control services, thermostats, access, ventilation and so on

- lighting services

- power services

- earthing services

- lightning protection services.

Each of these requires some mix of network types and has cabling requirements which need to co-habit with cabling for all the other applications.

## Eosys Cable Management Programme

Fourteen organisations with an active involvement in, and concern about, cabling joined Eosys in the Eosys Cable Management Programme. The fourteen organisations included:

```
AT & T
ARI Propaflor
Building Design Partnership
Central Computer and Telecommunications Agency
CEGB
Credit Suisse First Boston
Dorman Smith Britmac Ltd
Electricity Council
Honeywell Integrated Services Division
MOD-TAP Systems (UK)
Project Office Furniture
Sherfield (Investments) Ltd.
```

The objectives of the programme were to take a comprehensive approach to cabling and produce practical methodologies and tools for handling all aspects of all types of cabling throughout the life cycle of the installation.  These encompass recommended approaches for:

- the Cable Audit
- Cable Surveys
- Estimating and Costing for Cabling
- Cable Installation Specification
- Cable Marking and Documentation
- Overall Cable Management.

The increasing dependence of an organisation on cabling, combined with management inaction and ignorance add up to a high vulnerability.  The Eosys Cable Management Programme provides a way of minimising the risks and vulnerability, and of providing cost effective, well managed cabling installations.

# Designing for cabling requirements

Bill Southwood
Head of Communications
Ove Arup & Partners
London UK

Cable is an aspect of a building that tends to be forgotten...
until it becomes a problem. This paper addresses the actions
which can and should be taken in the design and construction
of new buildings to make them intelligent from a cabling
aspect. Cable entries, vertical and horizontal distribution,
fire and building regulations are considered. Coordination
with electrical and mechanical services is addressed along
with the need for specialised areas. Future trends are covered
and some guidlines given on how the need for cable management
can be communicated to those who will develop, design or
have to work in the building. The paper concludes with three
"model" buildings and the demands placed on them by communications
equipment.

Bill Southwood began his engineering
career in Sydney before taking up the
post of Director of Telecommunications
in Papua New Guinea.  Since joining
OVe Arup & Partners in London as head of
communications and information technology
he has advised developers, design teams,
owners and tenants on design and refurbishment of a wide range of buildings.

Presented at HIGH-TECH BUILDINGS 87: Online Publications, Pinner, UK, 1987

## INTRODUCTION

How many times have we been faced with the problems of installing some new piece of equipment in a building, creating the space for it, arranging for power and air conditioning, only to find that cabling presents an almost insurmountable problem? "Why could this not have been foreseen at the design stage?", is a valid question.

The reasons are many. Cable is a passive and unglamorous part of a high-tech building and tends to be forgotten until it forces itself on one's attention with the all too familiar effects: mountains of spaghetti, floor ducts full, risers clogged, ad hoc solutions piled on top of one another.

The purpose of this paper is to look at ways of designing buildings which are intelligent enough to cope with those cable systems which we can foresee and those which may evolve. After looking at distribution of cable in various zones, the paper considers cabling needs of specialist areas, building regulations, coordination with other services and the means of keeping the client informed. The problems of re-furbished buildings are considered as well as the case of the new design, and three model examples are introduced.

### Cable Entry into the Building

A truly intelligent building will allow its occupants for the life of the structure access to all forms of external communication. These will include the following services:

- duplicated entry for underground cables to ensure security
- access to alternative services such as BT and Mercury
- access to future services such as broadband cable
- off-air radio and tv reception
- reception of satellite broadcast
- two way satellite communication via small aperature terminals
- terrestrial microwave or laser communication

Entries will need to be appropriate to the diameters and bending radii of the cables being considered. It seems unlikely that any future requirement will be more stringent than the 100mm diameter ducts now used as standard to take multiple pair copper cables used in traditional telephony; certainly optical fibre cable fits readily within these parameters.

## Primary Distribution - the Vertical Riser

Risers are unpopular. To the developer they detract from net lettable floor area; to the fire officer they are a potential chimney to be stopped at all costs; to the occupant they are a mysterious network of caverns which show an alarming tendency to fill up with cable offcuts.

But adequate risers at appropriate points on the building plan, with access to cable entry points at basement and roof level, adjacent to equipment and computer rooms, and well coordinated between the competing services are an essential part of an intelligent building. The exact location and dimensions will depend on the plan shape and use to which the building will be put. Space on a side or rear wall for passive distribution frames, cable trays running the length of the riser, and a means of protecting the cable as it leaves the vertical run and starts its horizontal travels are vital.

## Secondary Distribution - Horizontally to the Workplace

There are many options available to distribute cabling from the riser to the plan position of the workplace, including:-

- distribution cn tray under a raised floor
- cable loose laid under raised floor
- cable in trunking under raised floor or in screed
- trunking cast into the floor slab
- perimeter trunking and partition distribution
- over-ceiling distribution with cable-carrying partitions or  "power poles" to bring services to the workplace

In the last few years we in the UK have come to accept a false floor as the hallmark of an intelligent building and, indeed, it does provide unparalled flexibility. This, of course, contains the seeds of its own downfall. A false floor has been seen as having such capacity as to obviate the need for good cable management with disastrous results. Whether the cable is laid on trays or loose laid, accurate recording of the routing of every cable under the floor is essential; equally important are the disciplines of requiring all installers to keep to defined routes, and recovering cables that are taken out of service.
Use of trunking under a false floor is a wasteful and restricting practice which is still surprisingly common. Raised flooring with integral trunking suspended from the jacks is an attractive idea, having the potential to do away with floor fixing for power cable and data tray. It remains to be seen whether it will become widespread.

Flush floor trunking as an alternative for a new building is adequate as long as it is positioned at close centres, no greater than 1.5m. It must also be provided with adequate routes into risers, calling for doubling up at congestion points. Trunking cast into the slab, as found in old buildings, is usually a disaster; if possible it should be cut out, and the chases so created used to grout in flush floor trunking.

In shallow building space in which a large proportion will be cellular offices rather than extensive open plan, perimeter trunking can be used to carry cable. Further trunking within furniture or partitions will carry power and communications to the workplace. This method is economical in cases where desks can be positioned either against a partition or in a contiguous line reaching the perimeter; it does limit changes, and militates against equipment on island sites.

Over-ceiling distribution is much more popular in Europe and the USA than in the UK. Disadvantages include the need for poles or wire-carrying partitions to carry cable to the work surface, the need for ladders (and therefore at least two fitters) to install or maintain cable and the fact that ceiling tiles will get dirty if removed frequently. On the other hand this method requires no false floor, and ceiling tiles do not get trapped under furniture!

Using the ceiling of one floor to serve desks on the floor above is severely limiting, and few occupants of the tenth floor can be expected to sympathise with someone on the eleventh whose need for a new terminal is filling their office with fitters and ladders.

Tertiary Distribution - from Building Envelope to Workplace

The method of reaching the work surface solves itself in the case of ceiling or perimeter distribution - underfloor distribution calls for special measures. The most visibly unacceptable face of unmanaged cable is the spider's web of power, telephone and data cable tangling its way from a floor outlet box via multiple power outlet blocks into the equipment on the desk.

Cable management furniture can solve the problem up to a point, although few of the desks currently on the market allow the flexibility of positioning and volume of cable routes needed.

Provision of pedestal: a vertical piece of trunking to bridge the gap from floor to work surface is an interesting recent development. Another is the use of a panel containing all connections which can be terminated prior to furniture being delivered, stored under the raised floor and attached to the underside of the desk subsequently.

## Specialised Areas: Frame and Equipment Rooms

It is customary and sensible to provide a room or rooms to house equipment frames in the basement of a building. If there are duplicated entry points for security, so should there be duplicated frame rooms. These need generally not be air conditioned as any active equipment housed in them is of very low consumption.

With increasing equipment to be mounted at roof level, it is sensible to allow for similar rooms at a high level in the building.

In a large development space adjacent to risers, in which patch cabinets can be mounted will allow maximum flexibility of use.

Specialist equipment and computer rooms require special treatment from the point of view of all the services. Cable management is no exception, and care must be taken to ensure that this point of greatest concentration does not, for all its depth of floor, become the point at which cable management fails.

## Alternatives in Re-furbished Buildings

Depending on its age, the building to be re-furbished will allow more or less scope for elegant cable management. The buildings of the 1950's and 60's with their very low slab to slab height, floor loading and environmental specification test one's ingenuity far more than their Georgian or Victorian ancestors. Existing buildings may have entrances and lobbies which have to be retained at their original level; ramping or stepping out of every lobby or service core is a dreadful legacy for the designer to leave the occupant.

In such cases intelligent cabling systems will take advantage of all of the techniques available for horizontal distribution. Provision of extra risers can usually be accomplished readily during a major re-furbishment, and this opportunity should be taken.

## Coordination with Electrical and Mechanical Services

Coordination is important at each stage of a design and during implementation. Cable entries must not clash with electricity, gas or water; risers must be shared with account being taken of likely problems of interference from power cables to communications; the distribution of small power will share the same horizontal space as the secondary voice and data cabling.

In the past such matters have been left to the electrical and mechanical engineers on the design and construction teams to sort out. In many cases this has resulted in excellent solutions; sometimes however we find that communication cable is left to fit in as best it can, causing difficulties.

The solution is to recognise the need for communications engineering expertise on the team at each stage of design and construction. This does now appear to be happening, and increasing numbers of developers and occupants now consider cable management before too much has been set in concrete.... literally!

## Alternatives to Cable

The dream of a cable-less building is unlikely to survive any awakening. Under-carpet systems which deny the third dimension is ultimately restricting, and the technology has practical difficulties.

Radiating systems based on infra-red transmission have even more fundamental objections. Firstly anything which unnecessarily increases the level of ambient radiation, by ever so small an amount, cannot be a good thing. Secondly, any receiver can be interfered with by another unwanted source. And finally, any system which radiates can be picked up by anybody who can mount a receiver within range ... undetectably.

Given the need to provide power at the workplace, it therefore seems an unnecessary extravagance to waste time on removing the communications cable.

## Communicating with the Client - Future Proofing

How can a professional team convince its client that such
obscure and tedious matters need consideration? How can we,
having sensitised the same client to the need for cable
management in building design, give some comfort that we have
got it right?

In one sense we have it relatively easy. Within the next few
years local area networks of baseband or broadband cable or
fibre will become both technically acceptable and affordable
for ordinary business, not just the largest and wealthiest.
When this happens we will have to overlay them on top of
existing systems of copper pair, coaxial, twinax, shotgun,
V24, current loop and every other imaginable system. If we
can design our buildings to take todays mass of wiring and
allow a bit of space over, and as long as those who follow
remember to recover the old cables when the new ones go in,
then today's properly designed buildings should see us into
the forseeable future.

Modern cable systems do not place greater demands on a
building than conventional copper cable. Fibre optic cable is
extremely tough and easier to install than multipair copper
cable. The minimum bending radius of a twelve fibre cable for
example is less than 1500mm. Some coaxial LAN cable is more
demanding with a large diameters and bending radius.
None the less this can be readily accommodated using the
techniques described earlier.

## Three Model Examples

There is no such thing as a "typical building"; even so it is
interesting to look at three models:

-   a conventional office, probably not in a city centre with
    a low penetration of communications and information
    technology

-   an office with a growing need for information technology

-   a city centre dealing operating in which information is
    central

The characteristics of these models are given in Table 1 below.

TABLE 1  -  WORKPLACE SERVICES

|  | General | IT | Dealer |
|---|---|---|---|
| Screens | 1/3 | 1 | 4 |
| Phones | 1 | 1-2 | Board |
| Calculator | 1 | 1 | 1 |
| Intercom | 1/3 | 1 | 1 |
| Equipment load (w/m²) (= heat) | 8 | 20 | 75-100 |
| Power sockets | 2-4 | 6 | 10+ |
| Lighting | Standard | Low glare | Special |
| Air Conditioning | Not required | Desirable | Essential |

The appropriateness of various method of distribution to the workplace are summarised in Table 2.


TABLE 2  -  SECONDARY DISTRIBUTION, WORKPLACE TO EQUIPMENT

|  | General | IT | Dealer |
|---|---|---|---|
| False floor | Nice | Desirable | Essential |
| Trunking centres | 2.5m | 1.5m | N/A |
| Perimeter + |  |  |  |
| - screens | OK ) | Limiting | N/A |
| - furniture | OK ) |  |  |
| Ceiling | Possible | Difficult | N/A |

Table 3 gives some guidelines for the cabling methods which may apply in our three models


TABLE 3  -  METHODS OF DISTRIBUTION INFORMATION

|  | General | IT | Dealer |
|---|---|---|---|
| Telepones | Yes | Yes | Yes |
| Density | 20pr/100m² | 40pr/100m² | Special |
| Computer Cable | As reqd. | Managed | Special |
| LAN | Soon | Now | Necessary |
| Voice/data PABX | Promising | "Casual" users | N/A |

It must again be emphasised that these typical examples should not be used to size a real building's power supply or air conditioning system - there is no substitute for a proper analysis of each case.

It is also likely that the "General" office example will disappear in time as it becomes the rule to have VDU's on desks and universal access to electronic information.

# Is there a common solution to cable management?

Ian C. Townsend
*Sales Manager*
**Ackermann Electrical Systems Limited**

The Hong Kong & Shanghai Bank and Lloyds of London building represent two of the most technically advanced buildings yet constructed. This paper sets out to demonstrate the level of detail that went into designing their cable management systems and how the experience gained from these projects can be applied to current designs. The paper also looks at how the service needs of a modern office can be accommodated through 'Loose Fit' technology.

**IAN TOWNSEND,** was appointed Sales Manager of the Electrical Products Division for Ackermann Electrical Systems Limited in 1986 and has been responsible for the development of the Company's Cable Management system.

Presented at HIGH-TECH BUILDINGS 87: Online Publications, Pinner, UK, 1987

# 1.0 REVIEW OF CURRENT TRENDS

Over the past two to three years the widespread use of
Raised Floors has dominated the way in which buildings
are cabled.

The often over-used but highly approriate title of
'Cable Management' very much describes the work with
which most of us are involved, and I think it fair to
say that the UK leads the world in this area of
technology.

Why should this be the case you may ask? And for the
answer, we must look to a number of factors:-

* the widespread use of Micro-Processors
* the ever increasing need for advanced
  telecommunications
* the development of the City of London as a Global
  Finance Centre
* the adoption of raised floors as a key factor in
  the letting of a building
* the continuing use of Open Plan Interiors

Looking at these factors in more detail is revealing,
for example:-

* The UK is the world leader in terms of the use of
  Raised Floors in office areas. In 1986
  approximately 1.2m sq.mtr were installed and this
  is set to increase in 1987.

* Currently there are in excess of 26 Raised Floor
  companies operating in the UK.

* Whilst Europe has gone away from Bureau Landschaft
  back to cellular offices, this has not happened in
  the UK, with major financial institutions looking
  for Open Plan areas (in some cases the size of
  football pitches) in order to accommodate their
  Dealing Rooms etc.

* The pace of change in the financial sector over the
  past few years has been outstanding with the influx
  of major overseas banking organisations each
  demanding the most up-to-date communication systems
  to enable them not only to keep up to date with
  what is happening in the market, but also to be
  able to deal globally, as the UK enjoys a unique
  time zone position between Tokyo and New York.

## 1.0    REVIEW OF CURRENT TRENDS (continued)

The method used for cabling has also changed with
the widespread use of networking for computers and
a less rigid and more flexible approach to telecoms
wiring since BT were liberized and introduced their
Plug and Socket System.

What are the trends that we are currently seeing in
Cable Management?

The primary method of Building Services Distribution
has, in fact, changed very little over the years with
the service riser providing the main means of vertical
distribution and being served from a basement switchroom
or similar.

Distribution within the office area itself has, however,
changed considerably. With the widespread adoption of
Raised Floors taking over from more rigid "In-Screed"
trunking systems.

The demise of the GLC has also affected the
installations being carried out in that there is no
longer a watchdog to ensure that certain standards are
being adhered to.

For example: In some installations within the City,
cables are simply being laid directly onto the slab
within the Raised Floor, with no attempt made to control
the routing of these cables and, indeed, no attempt to
segregate the cables of the various services.
Undoubtedly this type of installation is carried out
purely to cut costs; but does it?

Firstly, there is a good chance with this type of
installation, that it will become increasingly difficult
to identify cables - where they come from and where they
are going to - so, when any changes are necessary, the
labour involved with that change is going to cost more
than a well planned installation.

Secondly, indiscriminate cabling can also cost money in
other ways, for example, the integrity of the data
system may well become corrupted due to the proximity of
power lines or the possibility of data cables becoming
damaged due to abrasion with the rough surface of the
floor slab.

Finally, the system is far from flexible and may well
contravene Fire Standards.

## 1.0 REVIEW OF CURRENT TRENDS (continued)

The use of cable tray or trunking within the floor void ensures that the cables are protected and changes can be made to the system with the minimum amount of work or disruption.

Good installations require careful planning as, if insufficient cable routes are allowed, the system will become abused and if the density of trays/trunking hardware is too great, the installation will be unnecessarily expensive.

The increasing use of proprietory busbar systems within the floor void is indicative of the desire for greater flexibility on the part of the user and the need for quicker installation systems by the Electrical Contractors. Without similar tap-off networks for data and telecoms, however, the full potential of busbar systems cannot be realized. Our view is that concentrated tap-off units at pre-determined points within the Raised Floor offer as much flexibility as a continuous busbar, but without the cost burden.

## 2.0 THE HONG KONG & SHANGHAI BANK

It is interesting to examine in detail how two new and technically innovative buildings have developed their own Cable Management philosophy.

However, before moving forward to describe these two projects, it is necessary to stress the sheer commitment given by the respective Design Teams involved; particularly J. R. Preston & Partners in the case of the Hong Kong & Shanghai Bank and Ove Arup & Partners in respect of the Lloyd's project.

Both groups have endeavoured to achieve not only technical innovation, but also quality and good installation practice and it is this hard work which is reflected in what amounts to two of the best buildings around.

Most of you have had the opportunity to see Lloyd's; but probably not many The Hong Kong & Shanghai Bank. Should you be able to visit Hong Kong and see this building, you will not be disappointed but will be spellbound by the quality and level of detail which has gone into every single element of the building's design from the 'Sunscoop' to the 'Plant Room Hand Rails'.

## 2.0      THE HONG KONG & SHANGHAI BANK (continued)

We became involved with the Hong Kong & Shanghai Bank
when we were appointed by J.R.Preston & Partners and
Foster Associates to design a new floor box and to
prepare a design brief which could be used for
tendering.

Working closely with David Rigg of J. R. Preston &
Partners, one of the main criteria of the brief was that
the outlet should be circular and match the appearance
of the floor outlet air grilles being separately
developed by Trox Brothers Ltd, and work within a raised
floor.

### The Raised Floor

The Hong Kong & Shanghai Bank uses a Raised Floor, but a
Raised Floor which is very different from that currently
used in the United Kingdom.

Firstly, the raised floor panels were 1200mm x 1200mm
and constructed of a honeycombed aluminium core,
sandwiched between two flat aluminium sheets. The
technology was borrowed from the Aircraft Industry and
the panels are very strong and light and do not warp or
twist.

A number of panels were pre-cut with a circular hole to
accommodate either an air grille or floor outlets, as
both were identical in physical size and method of
installation.

The raised floor plenum was over 600mm deep to
accommodate substantial amount of air handling equipment
as well as providing a clear 100mm deep zone immediately
below the raised floor to accommodate electrical and air
outlets.

Cable distribution throughout the floor was achieved by
a network of multi-compartment trunking, serving in
excess of 6,000 No. Underfloor Distribution Boxes (UDU)
located on a pre-determined grid.

## 2.0      THE HONG KONG & SHANGHAI BANK (continued)

### The Design Brief

The design brief covered the electrical parameters plus a very stringent floor loading specification, such that the box needed to be able to withstand a point load of 5KN with a deflection of no more than 2mm.

It was also necessary to get air through the outlet to a series of local desk top air diffusers. Whilst eventually the localized air conditioning system was dropped from the building, the floor boxes still have the capability of accommodating a 50mm air tube.

The outlet was also required to accommodate:-

- 2 No 13A/240V unswitched power outlets
- 2 No 'D' type data connectors or BNC co-ax connectors
- 2 No shuttered Line Jacks
- 50mm Air Tube
- spare capacity for future data or telecomms connectors

and have the capability of being able to interchange the various accessories as, and when, required.

The box was also required to be manufactured of non-combustible materials.

### Design Solution

To achieve this very demanding specification, we developed a pressure die-cast aluminium base module which could be segmented to provide up to five individual compartments - separation between each compartment was by means of a removable PVC partition.

Accessory mounting plates were also made from PVC and could be positioned in any one of the five compartments.

The side walls of the die cast base had 3 No 25mm spouts each internally threaded to accept up to a 25mm diameter flexible conduit. The side wall adjacent to one of the segments also had a pre-cut hole to accommodate either an additional conduit or the 50mm diameter air tube.

## 2.0     HONG KONG & SHANGHAI BANK (CONTINUED)

### Design Solution (continued)

The power socket outlets were pre-wired at the factory with a multicore cable with moulded plug top and drawn through a 2.6m length of flexible conduit. The telephone and data compartments each had their own length of conduit fitted.

During the development of the Hong Kong & Shanghai Bank the Hong Kong Telephone Company was also looking at the possibility of changing from conventional wiring techniques to a plug + socket system (similar to that used by BT in the UK). The result was that we also had to develop a new version of the shuttered line jack which would be acceptable to the Hong Kong Telephone Company and the Bank. This was successfully achieved with a joint development between ourselves and Amphenol.

One particularly important requirement of this version of the shuttered line jack was, of course, that it needed to work in high levels of humidity.

A wide variety of data connectors were needed to be built into the floor boxes to service the very diverse range of Electronic equipment used by the Bank. These varied from 'D' Type connectors, through to very special connectors used for Dealing Room equipment.

The box also had to be quickly and easily installed and special attention was paid to this and a removable centre lifting pin provided.

The floor box covers were also required to suit specific floor environments which varied from carpeted to marble tiled areas, where waterproof versions of the floor outlet would be needed.

The type 'B' cover was the most common, and used in the carpeted office areas. Each outlet cover had a single wedge shaped electrical flex outlet with foam insert to prevent ingress of dust and dirt.

The Type 'C' cover had no facilities for cable exit and could be used to blank off any hole within the raised floor panel.

## 2.0    HONG KONG & SHANGHAI BANK (continued)

### Design Solution (continued)

The Type 'D' cover was a waterproof floor outlet for marble tiled areas with provision for a 13A waterproof socket which could be used by the cleaners. Access to the socket being gained by removing a centre screw-in section of the cover with a special tool.

The Type 'E' cover was, again, similar in design to the Type 'D' cover but complete with a 25mm high upstand collar, through which the cables passed. The base of the outlet was the standard five segment base unit complete with power, telephone and data accessories.

The Type 'F' covers was a waterproof version of the type 'C' cover and used to blank off any hole in the floor tile.

Whilst most of the outlet covers were hinged to allow easy access to the interior, others required a removable cover which could be secured in position using an Allenkey screw.

An extensive testing programme preceded the bulk manufacture of the floor outlets and a series of design load tests and wear tests formed an important part of the test programme.

The material used for the construction of the covers needed to be compatible in appearance and finish to that used on the Air Grilles, and following a detailed period of investigation it was agreed to use a aluminium.

Each cover was designed to have a series of concentric rings, the spacing of the rings matched those on the air grille and recesses were provided to simulate the equivalent position of slots on the air grille.

The surface of the cover was finished to give a smooth, but slightly grained look, which would stay bright. Each outlet cover was extensively tested for wear and load strength.

In all, five different types of cover were manufactured.

## 2.0     HONG KONG & SHANGHAI BANK (continued)

### Design Solution

At each stage of the Design, samples and prototypes were made and tests carried out to ensure that every aspect of the design brief was being met.  Finally, pre-production Prototypes were submitted to the client for approval.

In all, over 6,000 No. floor boxes were supplied to the Hong Kong Shanghai Bank, together with 6,000 underfloor distribution units.

### Underfloor Distribution Units

Each floor outlet box was supplied complete with conduits ready for interconnection to the Underfloor Distribution Boxes (UDU's).

Each UDU box was compartmented and contained six power socket outlets, three of which were connected to the clean earth supply and three to the normal supply. The power compartment also included an incoming terminal block and separate compartments were available for telephone and data respectively.

Due to the stringent fire standards imposed in Hong Kong, each box (UDU) had to be fully sealed and yet still allow conduits to be easily added to serve individual outlet boxes.

This was achieved by a purpose designed adaptor plate which would be clamped into the U-slot on the side of the floor outlet box.

Up to 9 No. 25mm dia flexible conduits could be connected to each UDU box.

Finally the UDU boxes were bolted to the 350 x 50mm trunking forming the secondary cable distribution network on a pre-determined grid.

## 3.0     LLOYD'S OF LONDON

Our involvement with the Lloyd's project did, in fact,
precede our work with the Hong Kong & Shanghai Bank; yet
the design of the floor box did not come until fairly
late in the contract, by which time we had completed a
substantial amount of the development work on the new
circular outlet box for the Hong Kong & Shanghai Bank.

The Lloyds project uses a Tate Raised Access Floor.

As the design brief for the floor outlets on Lloyds was
similar to that of the Hong Kong & Shanghai Bank, both
the Lloyd's Design Team as well as Lloyd's Management
themselves could see the benefits that had been built
into the new Hong Kong & Shanghai Bank box and wanted to
follow along much the same lines.

However, the air grilles being used on Lloyd's were
constructed of Nylon and not aluminium and it was,
therefore, necessary for us to develop a new top lid
section which could be combined with the new base box
being developed for the Hong Kong & Shanghai Bank.

The requirement for power, data and telecommunications
in both buildings was, of course, very similar and based
on almost identical specification for individual
accessories.

Lloyd's, however, required a greater range of floor box
interior design configurations with both standard and
non-standard power socket outlets being used and which
could be connected to either an Essential or Non-
Essential supply.

On Lloyd's, as on the Hong Kong & Shanghai Bank, pre-
wired flexible conduits were used to connect the boxes
back to the sub- floor distribution system. Sockets were
wired on both, ring and radial circuits, and connected
back to a terminal block enclosed in a steel box
adjacent to the sub-floor distribution trunking network.

Over 15,000 metres of trunking was used to form a cable
management network which could service in excess of
3,000 floor outlet boxes.

The complexity of other services within the raised floor
void meant that the floor trunking had to be tailor made
to fit with a variety of ramps, bends, offsets etc.

## 3.0    LLOYD'S OF LONDON (continued)

A primary network of 500mm x 100mm deep four compartment trunking was used to link each floor back to three separate service risers.

From the primary distribution route, 150mm x 75mm three compartment secondary trunking runs were served.

The Lloyd's building is a section twenty building and, therefore, as on the Hong Kong & Shanghai Bank, all the floor trunking and floor boxes needed to be constructed of a non-combustible material.

### HIGH LEVEL SERVICES

A distinctive feature of Lloyd's are the external services and these were extended inside the building to the high level trunking running through the coffers, where a series of circular aluminium trunking sections were used to service luminaires and ancillary equipment.

Ackermann manufactured and prepared a complete network of circular trunking varying in size from 75mm through to 125mm. The trunking is two-compartment and at each junction, cross-over units needed to be developed which, not only allowed the cables to cross fully segregated from one section to another, but also enabled changes in level to occur.

The circular trunking had removable covers, and tap offs, for flexible conduits, were provided every 1500mm to feed each luminaire.

## 4.0    NEW DEVELOPMENTS IN CABLE MANAGEMENT TECHNIQUES

It is fair to say that whilst the two projects were technically innovative, they were both very expensive, but have given the lead way to develop new products which can provide the same facilities and benefits, but at a much lower cost.

The principle design features that both projects embodied were:

. The flexibility offered by pre-wired floor boxes.
. A network of trunking within the raised floor that can accommodate change.
. Floor boxes with tested design load performance.

## 4.0    NEW DEVELOPMENTS IN CABLE MANAGEMENT TECHNIQUES (continued)

### The Advantages of Pre-wired Floor Boxes

The main advantages of pre-wiring the boxes are:

. lower costs
. faster installation times
. higher standards of quality

The lower costs are achieved due to the fact that the floor box manufacturer purchases flexible conduit and fittings in much higher quantities than would be needed on an individual project.

The manufacturer is also installing the conduits and wiring them to the sockets under factory controlled conditions using assembly line techniques. Compare this with an Electrician with a roll of conduit on his arm, a pocket full of fittings who then needs to install and wire the conduits, on his knees, onto an already installed floor box.

The increasing use of pre-wired busbars within the raised floor has further strengthened the need for quick and flexible installation techniques.

By designing a floor box with a base module which can be pre-wired, we also have a box which can be easily changed from one position to another, with the minimum amount of work and disruption.

Above all, the benefit of pre-wired base modules ensures fast installation on site, where time is often the essence.

### Trunking Networks

Within offices, people, furniture and partitions are constantly changing. British Telecom, for example, estimate that within the first year of a building being occupied, up to 50% of the telephones are moved. New technology is also creating new demands and one only has to think back a few years when telephones were only provided to senior managers.

## 4.0   NEW DEVELOPMENTS IN CABLE MANAGEMENT TECHNIQUES
## (continued)

### Trunking Networks (continued)

A well designed cable management system, therefore, needs to ensure that changes can be easily made and that the system can be expanded.

Whilst raised floors offer the space in which to run cables to provide this flexibility, all too often the space is restricted by other services, or constraints on the height of the floor itself.

There appears to be no common standard for the height of a raised floor, but 150mm seems to be more the norm than other heights. When allowing for the thickness of the floor tile itself, this leaves a clear void depth of between 100-120mm, depending on the tolerance of the slab and floor tile construction.

### Typical Methods of Cable Installation

There are several ways in which cables can be run within the raised floor void:

. enclosed in the trunking
. on the cable tray
. direct onto the slab

It is also important to consider the height at which the cables are run:

. either directly on the slab where it would be necessary to form bridges so that other cables and services can cross over.

. or directly beneath the tile so that other cables and services can cross underneath.

There are also systems available which intergrate flush floor trunking within the raised floor itself. Whilst the cost of these systems can, to a large extent, be offset by the reduced number of floor tiles needed, they are quite expensive and difficult to install. The PSA's specification MOB 801 also sets very strict design loads for raised floors and this is very difficult to achieve with cost effective integrated trunking systems.

**4.0**   **NEW DEVELOPMENTS IN CABLE MANAGEMENT TECHNIQUES (continued)**

Typical Methods of Cable Installation (continued)

Our view is that it is better to leave the raised floor intact and provide a lower cost cable management system within the raised floor itself and which can be installed as part of the raised floor, or independently on the floor slab.

One of the advantages of the trunking or tray installed directly beneath the tile is that is gives immediate access and leaves space beneath for other services.

For flexibility one also has to consider how the floor outlet boxes can be connected to the cable management network.

One advantage of the pre-wired floor box is that it can be plugged into a proprietary busbar system thus keeping installation time and thus costs down to a minimum.

We ourselves have developed a hybrid between a trunking and tray system, which makes full use of the space between the floor tile pedestals and allows the underside of the floor tile to form the lid of the centre Power compartment.

The half length side walls and perforated centre partitions make the termination of cables and conduits simple and effective.  The system can accommodate busbars, or traditional cabling techniques.

Conventional trunking laid within the raised floor void may appear to be the easiest and obvious solution, but is becoming increasingly uncompetitive against the newer, more flexible system on the market.

## 4.0     NEW DEVELOPMENTS IN CABLE MANAGEMENT TECHNOLOGY (continued)

### Design Load Performance

Floor boxes have traditionally presented problems with regard to their lids bending and carpets around the edges becoming frayed.

For raised floors the floor box design also needs to be considered in conjunction with the PSA's specification MOB 801 which defines particularly the point load requirements with which the raised floor has to comply.

It is important that any floor outlet box located within a raised floor is able to withstand, as near as possible, similar loading standards, to the floor itself.

In the absence of a British Standard for the boxes, our boxes were recently tested by the British Board of Agrement in order to assess their load strengths and as a result of this we have received a Certificate No. 86/1774 which confirms the suitability of our floor boxes for use within raised floors.

We also carried out our own tests on a number of different outlet boxes and found that the lid deflection varied substantially.

Therefore in specifying floor outlet boxes it is very important to consider not only the service requirements, but also the duty requirement and to specify the minimum deflection you require to achieve for a given point load.

## 5.0     THE FUTURE FOR RAISED FLOORS

We have seen the wide spread adoption of raised floors as the solution to Cable Management and most of this paper has been devoted to how cable management with raised floors is being done but, raised floors are enormously expensive when applied throughout a major building.

There is also a great deal of difference between the capabilities of individual floor tile systems, both in terms of flexibility and stability.

## 5.0    THE FUTURE FOR RAISED FLOORS (continued)

Many raised floors have also become misused with cables being run uncontrolled and poorly protected.

A number of major companies and Architectural practices are therefore, looking towards what can be done to provide Cable Management <u>without</u> the use of raised floors and we, ourselves, are involved with several product development exercises, which would negate the use of raised floors altogether, and can foresee and believe that, whilst at the present time raised floors offer the best solution to Cable Management, the future holds the opportunity for a much wider range of products; products which are more closely geared to providing Cable Management within the furniture itself.

On the development recently completed for BICC's, Data Networks Company, groups of desks were connected together to form multi-workstations and where each desk is served by a Desklink panel containing power/telephone sockets, as well as through cable routes. Each desk also has within it power, data and telephone distribution capabilities.

Above all, the cables are hidden and spare or excess cable can be easily tidied up.

## 6.0    LOOSE FIT SERVICES TECHNOLOGY

We would define this type of product as 'Loose Fit' Technology, where by using carefully designed and integrated cable management products, a less expensive and more flexible system can be achieved.

Such 'Loose Fit' Systems are also more responsive to the needs of the end user and, of course, less expensive for the developer who would not need to concern himself with the high capital cost of either planning for or, indeed, providing the raised floor itself.

At the present time the specifier has little to choose from, but in the age of electronics the pace of change is much more rapid than before and we may soon be talking about 'Loose Fit' rather than Hi-tech Cable Management.

\*    \*    \*    \*    \*    \*

# Integrated cabling systems:
# a step in the right direction?

Paul Taylor
Senior Consultant
CHA Networks Limited
England

This paper discusses the desirable attributes of an integrated cabling system, and compares three specific examples, before evolving a generally applicable vendor-independent approach, acknowledging the requirements of a variety of DP systems, whilst remaining flexible and capable of expansion.

As Senior Consultant with CHA Networks, Paul Taylor has responsibility for integrating major data communications projects in the multi-vendor environment, so often found in large companies today.

Presented at HIGH-TECH BUILDINGS 87: Online Publications, Pinner, UK, 1987

## Integrated Cabling Systems - A step in the right direction ?

As we approach the 1990's, it is more than ever true that a company's performance depends vitally on the fast and effective communication of information between individuals and machines. This paper seeks to analyse the new wave of integrated cabling systems on offer from three of the major vendors, and how they impinge on a company's communications strategy, both now and in the future.

Historically, data cabling has been of secondary concern to computer vendors, and each has evolved numerous solutions specific to his own equipment, with little regard for inter-working or standardisation. Hence the common twisted pair cable competes with coaxial, twin-axial, broadband and fibre optic cabling in a plethora of poorly integrated 'one-off' links between remote resources and their users.

It has become obvious in recent years, both to vendors and their customers, that such approaches, in isolation, do not address the true needs of corporate data communications strategy. Increasingly, we see a scenario in which distributed machine intelligence, from the personal computer, to the departmental mini-computer, to the corporate mainframe, requires high capacity data links with high connectivity to multiple local and remote resources.

At a time when the value of global PC sales is now outstripping mainframe sales, it is essential that flexible, high speed communications are available to all users within an organisation. To this end, a number of major vendors have started to promote "integrated cabling systems", based on the needs of their own product line, but claiming wider applications for corporate data, voice and image distribution.

Before comparing the approaches adopted by the vendors, let us consider the desirable attributes of an integrated cabling system (ICS). These include:

* Maximising the percentage of cabling work carried out during building construction, avoiding re-work and disruption after occupation,

* Integration of all telephone, data and image
  (video) transmission services at the user interface
  (faceplate),

* High penetration of work areas, to reduce local
  cabling to a minimum,

* High data-carrying capacity to each ´information
  outlet´,

* Easy configuration, to allow every point access to
  a range of services,

* Easy re-configuration, to allow high mobility of
  users,

* Transparency to communications protocols or
  topologies, allowing vendor-independence,

* Cost effective support for both simple (terminal)
  and complex connections,

* Capacity for planned growth, to encompass future
  requirements for traffic and connections.

Let us briefly consider this last point, as it is
probably the most crucial in ensuring that a building´s
cabling system facilitates, rather than dictates, a
company´s communications structure.  At present, most
data devices support one of four generic connection
types:

a)  A low speed (up to around 50 kbps) terminal
    or printer interface, e.g. RS232, RS422,

b)  A high speed (around 1 to 4 Mbps) channel
    connection, e.g. IBM coax ´A´,

c)  A high speed contention network connection
    e.g. Ethernet, at 10 Mbps,

d)  A high speed deterministic network connection
    e.g. Token Ring at 4 Mbps.

Of these, all but c) are supported directly on simple
twisted pair wiring, and all four are possible via
coaxial and fibre optic cables and appropriate
interface units.

Future requirements will almost certainly call for
higher speed connections to each workstation, either in
the form of fast ´browsing´ access to databases
(needing tens of megabits per second), or videophone
links.  It would be imprudent, therefore, to assume
that a cable system capable of supporting a few
megabits per second will be adequate for all projected
needs within, say, ten years.

We will now consider each of the proprietory solutions,
in the context of the above remarks.

IBM Cabling System

This system has evolved in parallel with the
introduction of IBM´s Token Ring Network for connecting
PC´s.  It seeks to bring the benefits of an integrated
cabling philosophy to the diverse range of connection
techniques currently in use for IBM devices, including
coaxial, twin-axial and loop connections.

Based on radially connected, dual twisted-pair cables
to each data outlet, it makes use of the ability of
such a cable to carry high speed data (up to around
4 Mbps) over moderate distances within a distribution
area.  A single "unisex" connector type is used,
simplifying the assembly of cables and faceplates.

At the centre of the distribution area, rack-mounted
distribution panels use patch cords to configure each
individual user faceplate for one of a number of
different services, such as cluster, token ring or loop
connected controllers.

At the faceplate, a series of adaptor cables (baluns)
are available to convert signals on the twisted pair
(BALanced) medium, to coaxial or twin-axial
(UNbalanced) cables, as required.

This system can thus be seen to meet most of the
requirements for a general purpose ICS, but the special
connector type and range of adaptor cables are specific
to IBM connections, and the exclusive use of twisted
pair cabling to the workstation could limit long term
information capacity.

## The DECconnect concept

The Digital approach to integrated cabling takes the process somewhat further than IBM´s. Instead of using a single medium and connector type, DECconnect recognises that no one physical medium is likely to be able to solve all connection problems in the most cost effective manner, and provides each faceplate with a combination of separate baseband coaxial, broadband coaxial and multi-function twisted pair cables, for data, voice and video services.

As before, a centrally located patching system is used to route services to the appropriate faceplate; the difference between this and IBM´s system is that no media transition is needed at the faceplate, as each required cable type is in place already.

This multi-media approach is driven by Digital´s two principal connection philosophies - firstly, the use of twisted pairs between terminals and network servers, and secondly, the linking of Ethernet (10 Mbps) devices by coaxial cables. Most applications would call for a combination of these two, depending on the ratio of terminals to intelligent processors within a department.

Clearly, the provision of such multi-media cabling will attract a cost penalty with respect to those systems solely involving twisted pair cabling, but will have the advantages of flexibility and capacity for expansion.

## The AT & T approach

The AT & T cabling system, known as the Premises Distribution System (PDS), uses a combination of twisted pair and fibre optic cables in a structured approach to building cabling. For most purposes, it applies a similar concept of radially connected twisted pairs running from local distribution frames, but teams this with the use of fibre optic multiplexers for IBM and asynchronous links. Local cable balun adaptors, similar to IBM´s, are used for media conversion, and matching to third party equipment (e.g., Wang).

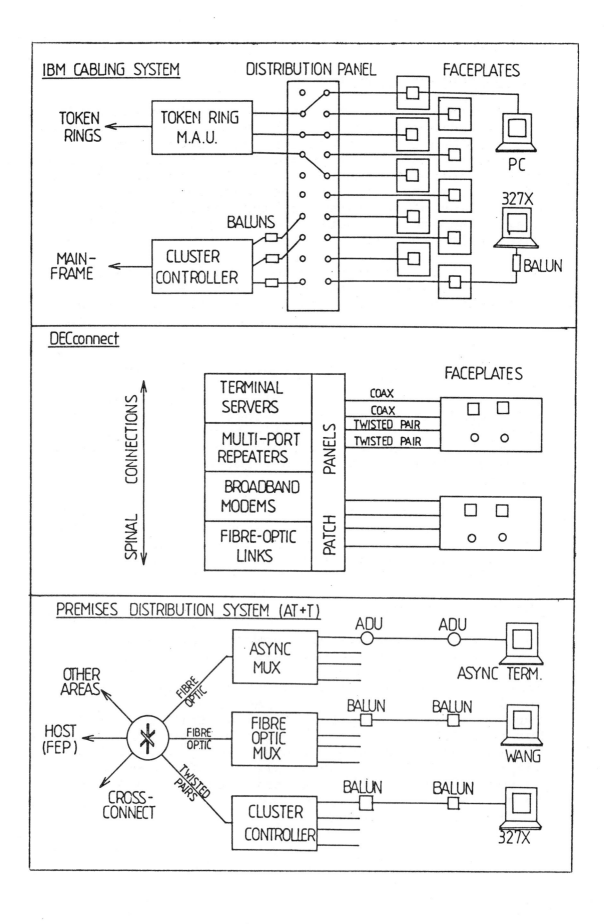

Tying in with AT & T´s own range of LAN products,
links between distribution areas are realised either
as point-to-point fibre cabling, or as multiple,
switched twisted pairs.  Where extended runs of twisted
pair cabling are proposed, asynchronous data units
(ADU´s) or synchronous data units (SDU´s) are used as
line drivers.

The approach is thus seen to be more flexible in its
support of multi-vendor equipment than IBM´s, with
direct implementation of a wider range of interfaces.
However, these in turn can be a barrier to
communications if not fully protocol independent,
or of sufficiently high speed. It´s basis in twisted
pairs will ensure easy integration with PABX equipment,
and a lower cost than a more comprehensive, multi-media
system.

## Spinal Connection Technologies

Before considering a vendor-independent solution to
integrated cabling, we must address the issue of spinal
connections.  We have seen how each of the proprietory
systems create a single service point (we shall call it
a communications distribution centre, or CDC), for all
users within its coverage area.  This, in itself, will
allow each of these users full access to resources
within their own department, but does not address the
accessing of either other departments of central
resources.

As the volume and speed of data transfer increases, the
choice of spinal technology to address these needs
becomes crucial if a ´corporate log-jam´ is to be
avoided.  It is in the choice of such technology that
questions of specific vendors´ equipment and connection
topologies become important.

The accompanying diagram shows three alternatives for
spinal connections within a building; star, bus or mesh
connections. Each has its own merits amd may be best
suited to a particular communications structure.  The
important point to grasp here is that flexibility in
selecting the spinal connections leaves the way open
for each of the specific systems previously considered
to be implemented to its best advantage.

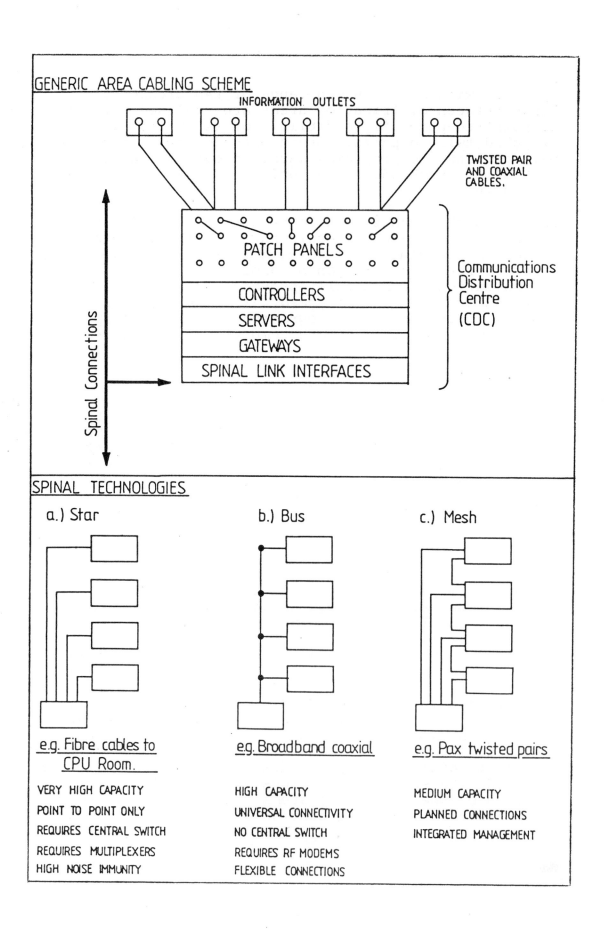

GENERIC AREA CABLING SCHEME

INFORMATION OUTLETS

TWISTED PAIR AND COAXIAL CABLES.

PATCH PANELS

Communications Distribution Centre (CDC)

CONTROLLERS

SERVERS

GATEWAYS

SPINAL LINK INTERFACES

Spinal Connections

SPINAL TECHNOLOGIES

a.) Star

b.) Bus

c.) Mesh

e.g. Fibre cables to CPU Room.

e.g. Broadband coaxial

e.g. Pax twisted pairs

VERY HIGH CAPACITY

POINT TO POINT ONLY

REQUIRES CENTRAL SWITCH

REQUIRES MULTIPLEXERS

HIGH NOISE IMMUNITY

HIGH CAPACITY

UNIVERSAL CONNECTIVITY

NO CENTRAL SWITCH

REQUIRES RF MODEMS

FLEXIBLE CONNECTIONS

MEDIUM CAPACITY

PLANNED CONNECTIONS

INTEGRATED MANAGEMENT

This allows local area distribution cabling to be implemented fully during building construction, whilst connections in central risers may be added to later, or subsequently re-defined to meet changing needs.

## The Vendor-Independent Approach

If the client's DP systems at the time of occupation of the building are perceived to be met by one of the proprietory systems discussed, there is a great temptation to follow the scheme to the letter. As we have seen, this can lead to the client being locked into a particular vendors' product line, and may well limit his ability to take advantage of new technology as it is developed.

We have seen how each of the systems contain some of the desirable features of a universally acceptable scheme, such as low cost twisted pair cabling, high capacity coaxial or fibre optic cabling, protocol-free manual patching systems and modular connectors. It would seem reasonable, therefore, in those instances where vendor-independence is desired of a new cable installation, that a combination of multi-function twisted pair and coaxial cabling be installed a to multi-point data outlet, preferably serving telephone connections as well. Connections from faceplates to the CDC's would still be manually patched into a variety of data interface equipment, such as controllers, servers and multiplexers, which in turn would connect to a choice of spinal technologies, the latter being chosen to suit the chosen vendor(s) network topology, (whether it be star-wired, bus-oriented or mesh-connected), the required degree of connectivity between areas and the data throughput needed. Should a change of DP strategy or tenant occur at a later date, the implications in terms of cabling should then extend only as far as the CDC's, protecting the investment in local area cabling. Experience of the recent rapid growth in the demands of computer users, for faster and more accessible services, has shown the perils of under-provision of connections of sufficient flexibility and capacity to soak up these demands, in terms of full cable ducts and costly re-work for minor extensions.

# ISDN: what, more networks?

Roger Camrass
Director of Consultancy
Butler Cox & Partners Limited
United Kingdom

The immediacy of internal networking problems has caused
many organisations to tackle the effects rather than the
causes of congestion within building wiring.  The
prospect of even more rapid growth in demand for internal
network connections could frustrate management still
further in the near future.  Rather than provide short-
term remedies, this paper focuses on the emerging
integrated network approaches able to accommodate both
short and longer term requirements within the local
office.

Roger Camrass is director of
consultancy with Butler Cox.  Prior
to this, he was responsible for
telecommunications studies and the
development of a building technology
practice providing specialised
services to developers and tenants
of high-tech buildings.

Presented at HIGH-TECH BUILDINGS 87: Online Publications, Pinner, UK, 1987

ISDN - WHAT, MORE NETWORKS?

## Tackling the cause, not the effect

The increasing numbers and diversity of workstations in
the office have placed an almost impossible burden on
local network facilities.  As a result, most managers are
searching desperately for some means of responding to
increasing user pressure for more termination points, and
corresponding underfloor wiring.  The immediacy of the
problems inhibits any longer term planning or network
provision.  Many managers are resigned to the prospect
that things must get worse before they can get better.

However, an increasing number of organisations are now so
seriously concerned with the inadequacy of local
communications facilities that they are considering major
refurbishments, and in some extreme cases a complete
relocation.  At the same time, systems departments are
analysing more flexible ways of providing local
communications facilities, including the wide scale
adoption of local area networks.

To overcome the chaos developing at the cabling level,
and to meet the growing expectations of users for
flexible communications facilities, managers responsible
for local networking will need to tackle the underlying
requirements rather than to struggle on with ad hoc,
fragmented solutions that have long since outgrown their
usefulness.

## Understanding the requirements

The networks and supporting cabling schemes currently
installed within large offices largely reflect a systems
environment of the 1970s rather than the late 1980s.
Much of this wiring has been built up around mainframe
and stand alone departmental mini computers with the
result that isolated user communities have access to
dedicated computer resources.

## Figure 1:  Networks supporting first generation users

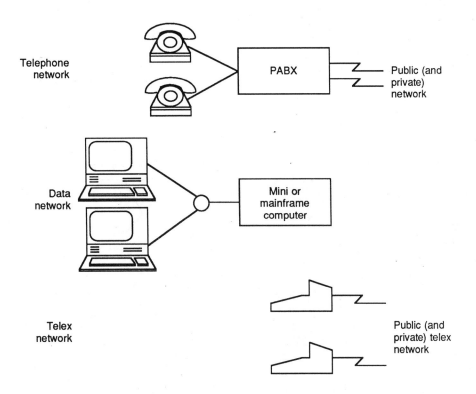

In today's systems environment, growing emphasis is being
placed on providing a multiplicity of services to each
end user, which in turn implies wider interconnection
of systems.  In such environments, voice and data are still
likely to remain apart, but a high degree of network
integration is evident amongst non voice services.

Figure 2:   Networks supporting third generation users

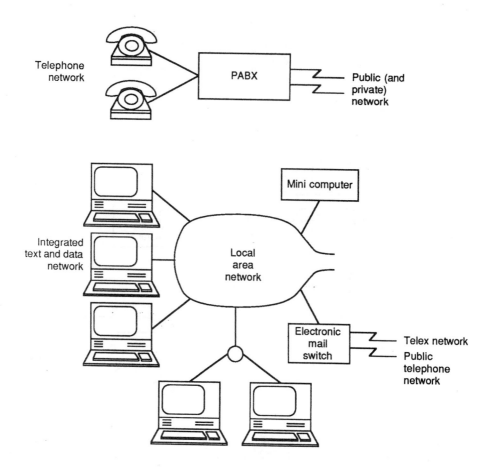

In addition to the emphasis on interconnection, terminals themselves are becoming more sophisticated, with a wide adoption of personal computers in place of traditional dumb screens.  This trend is likely to continue well into the nineties, with the ultimate prospect of a multi media workstation being only a few years away.

Figure 3:   Evolution of multifunction workstations

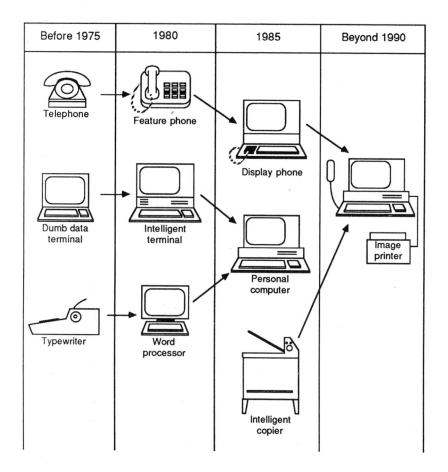

Overlaid on these fundamental system and network trends
are the practical demands of the modern office, including
the regular movement of staff around the building, and
the growing congestion of ducts and risers due to the
proliferation of cables.

Any networking scheme designed to overcome current wiring
problems within the office will need to provide a
multiplicity of services to all information workers -
managers, secretaries, professionals and clerks,
regardless of physical location.  This calls for a unified
network approach quite different to that found in many
offices today.

Figure 4:  The growing range of services implies a
           continuous spectrum of network requirements

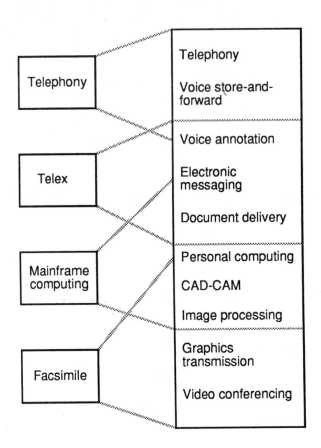

## Evaluating the network options

A typical modern office block today will employ several
proprietary network approaches.  These may include:

-   Twisted pair block wiring for telephony.

-   Dedicated coax cable for dumb data terminals
    connected to a mainframe.

-   Shielded twisted pair for local mini computer
    terminals.

-   One or more proprietary local area network
    (eg Ethernet, Token Ring).

Each new computer system is likely to introduce yet
another independent network with its own cabling and
distribution points.

To overcome the growing volumes and diversity of cabling
to support these independent systems, at least four integrated networking schemes are becoming available, each of
which offers a sizeable reduction in the number of local
networks.

1. Data-over-voice: This scheme exploits existing
   twisted pair cable installed for telephony purposes
   by deriving a separate data path. A simple line
   driver or multiplexor is required at each telephone
   extension point. The advantage of this scheme is
   its ability to exploit existing block wiring.
   However, transmission speeds are limited (up to
   19.2 K bps), and cost per connection is high.

Figure 5: Data-over-voice

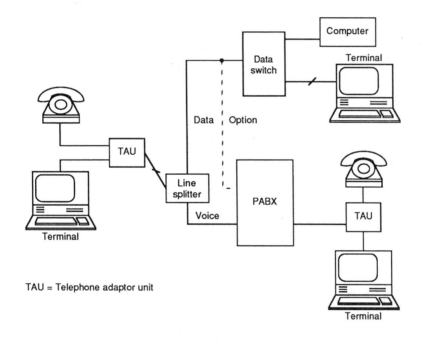

2. Integrated voice/data: The advent of digital PABXs
   and ISDN transmission and switching standards may
   encourage wider use of the telephone network for
   supporting internal and external data connections.
   However, the technology is still relatively embryonic
   with less than 1% of installed PABXs offering
   integrated connection.

Figure 6:   Integrated voice and data

3.   Integrated cabling schemes:  Here, each work position
     is wired with a common cabling scheme, frequently
     combining telephony and data within a single sheath.
     Inherent within this approach is a local wiring
     closet containing a flexible patch panel to enable
     full interconnection.  A few important schemes are
     emerging on the market.  However, the approach calls
     for substantial alteration to a building - such as
     the inclusion of a false floor.

Figure 7:   Universal wiring schemes

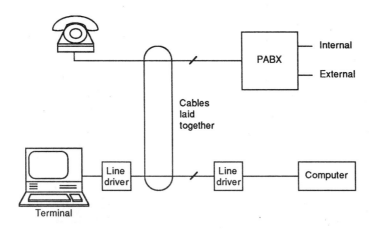

4.   Local area network (LAN):  Although not mutually
     exclusive with 3., this approach frequently implies a
     separate data cable installed around a building, see
     Figure 8.  The advantage of a LAN is the high level of
     function available, and the relatively modest amount
     of wire.  Already 10% of installed terminals are
     connected to LANs.  Up to 50% could be connected by
     the early nineties.

Figure 8:   Local area networks

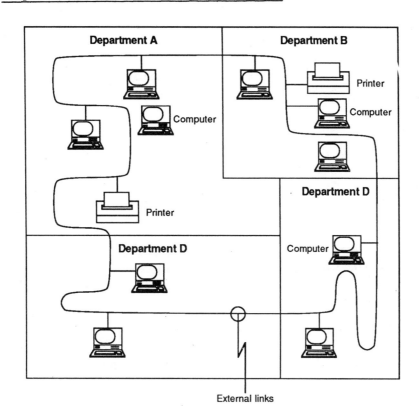

Selecting a suitable network approach

The choice of a suitable network approach depends on several factors, the most important of which are likely to be the state of the existing building, and the nature of the computing facilities to be supported by the network.

For the present time, little benefit is likely to be derived from bringing together voice and data within a single integrated network.  However, a common cabling scheme does have considerable appeal, especially where a major refurbishment or relocation is being planned.

The use of a single cabling technology, eg fibre, coax or twinax, throughout a building should improve network flexibility, especially where 100% prewiring is practical.  Care must be taken over cable management and physical termination interfaces (eg impedance matching).

Finally, attention must always be given to system plans, as and when they become available for discussion. The relationship between networking technology and systems approach is becoming stronger as more intelligence is being devolved out to the user terminal. In many situations, little progress can be made at the cabling level until the systems approach is fully defined.

## Planning a building network

The wiring chaos ensueing in many buildings today emphasises the need for long-term planning and coordination in network development. To be effective in this area, management should consider the following recommendations.

- Organise cabling and local networking under one line manager, or user steering committee. Frequently, several different departments have responsibility for cabling today.

- Strengthen links between systems and telecommunications planners. Dialogue should be two-way, especially where systems plans are still ill-defined.

- Press senior management into making a sizeable up-front investment in a flexible building network, especially during refurbishment or relocation. Much money can be wasted in retaining fragmented facilities.

- Ensure ongoing management of cabling networks, with automated inventory and cost monitoring procedures.

No organisation can suddenly rectify the problems implicit in its local networks. However, prompt action today can ensure resolution of these problems within two to three years. This will be of real benefit to all those who occupy the building and manage the internal services.

# The emergence of the intelligent office building in North America, Japan & Europe

Dr Francis Duffy
Partner, DEGW Architects Space Planners Designers
London, Glasgow, Paris, Milan, Mexico City

The path of development for intelligent buildings varies considerably from continent to continent according to requirement and understanding of the term 'intelligent building'. The major factor that is relevant to all continents and types of intelligent buildings is responsiveness to change, the buildings ability to accommodate over time change in individual requirements and organisational demands.

Founding and senior partner with particular interest in helping clients use space over time. Co-author of Planning Office Space (Arch. Press 1975 and 1986); led the ORBIT 1 and 2 studies on impact of IT on buildings in the UK and US; editor of Facilities. Founder Building Use Studies.

Presented at HIGH-TECH BUILDINGS 87: Online Publications, Pinner, UK, 1987

## A Wider Context

Lack of depth in the usual price paid for breath of ambition.
However, in order to make sense of the current enthusiasm for the
Intelligent Office Building it is necessary not only to investigate
what is happening in countries as widely dispersed as Japan, Sweden
and the United States but also to indulge in a rather liberal
interpretation of what office buildings actually are.  The first
benefit of this point of view is that a great deal can be learned by
architects and clients from contrasts between offices built in
different countries (and for different organisations) particularly
about values held by the individuals and about the social structures
which make up the modern office organisation.  The second benefit is
that a better understanding of how offices are built and serviced,
through time, is of great practical advantage to those who must manage
rapidly changing organisations.

The phrase "Intelligent Building" means many things to many different
people.  A futuristic view would lead one to imagine buildings which
had learned to walk towards the sun, or away from its burning rays,
depending upon the latitude for which they were built; buildings which
could anticipate not only the extremes of climate but also the likely
pattern of diurnal use so that scarce energy could be expended with
the utmost parsimony; buildings which know where everything and
everyone was at any time of day or night; buildings which recognise
you and are sufficiently clever to hand you your raincoat and umbrella
when you leave the door not because they don't know it is sunny in
London but because they have learned from your diary that you are off
on a trip to Manchester where rain, it so happens, is falling today.
Let Professor Walter Kroner, the architect and futurist, director of
the Centre for Architectural Research at Rensselaer Polytechnic
Institute in Troy, New York, have the last futuristic word:
"Buildings haven't changed since Stonehenge.  A truly intelligent
building would be one that can anticipate conditions and forces acting
on the building.  Such a building may change its colour, envelope
configuration, orientation, and composition.  They could float in
water, rise up and go down into the ground, or rotate.  Theoretically
you could build a building out of paper because the forces of nature
would no longer act on the building but on a protective superstructure
above the City".

Although Kroner's speculations are far from unrealisable, it is best
to push them aside for the moment because they are so entertaining
that they obscure several other themes in building intelligence which
are much discussed but often confused.

## Four Dimensions of Building Intelligence

The clearest, if not absolutely the most complete, exposition of these themes is contained in an excellent document produced, naturally enough, in Japan, by the newly deregulated and privatised Nippon Telegraph & Telephone Company (NTT, the Japanese BT).  NTT distinguishes three major aspects of building intelligence:

1.  Office Automation - a high level of Office Automation provided by the building owner, either for his own organisation's use, or for tenants.  Such features include built in Local Area Networks (LANs or data highways to use a more colourful expression) together with a wide selection of high tech office equipment such as  word processing, large volume printing, electronic filing, electronic diaries, credit card access for timekeeping or for access to cafeteria and common office services, software support, and even "War Rooms" where data is assembled and manipulated in electronic form for big decision makers.

2.  Advanced Telecommunications - The potential offered to tenants or user organisations to have ready access to a far more up-to-date and wider range of telecommunication services than they would customarily expect.  This wider range is achieved through digital switching and fibre optic cabling and leads not only to considerable advantages in volume and cost but also to particular services such as facsimile, voice mail, computer graphics, as well as voice, video and computer conferencing.

3.  Building Automation - The oldest and most reliable form of building intelligence which is based upon the integration, through electronics, of various subsystems useful for running buildings such as building management, security of people, power, and data, as well as energy.

    NTT are quick to point out, not only in their documentation but also in their prototypical intelligent building projects, such as their new Shinagawa complex, that these three aspects of intelligent building have important implications for the way in which buildings are planned and managed (eg. emerging methodologies in Facilities Management and Space Planning) as well as in the development of new kinds of building components (better ducting systems for cables and air conditioning, more responsive lighting and furniture, building skins which react to light) and building techniques (life cycle costing, fast tracking of construction, greater responsiveness to changing demands).

    There is an irony here.  Despite this wonderful shopping list, the reality is that the kinds of office buildings currently occupied by organisations such as Honda, Mitsubishi, Mitsui, Daiwa, Toshiba, Shimuzu are not only crushingly similar but, by advanced

Western standards, elementary not just in quality but also in the application of information technology to office tasks. For a variety of complicated reasons (not least of which is the refractory nature of the Japanese language, especially its characters) the bulk of office technology used in Japan tends to be centralised and top down rather than distributed and dynamic. Hence the environmental stress generated in many Western organisations by PCs and LANs seems still rare in Japan.

Perhaps this is why NTT fail to mention what seems to us in DEGW to be a colossally important aspect of building intelligence.

4.  Responsiveness to Change - The ability of buildings to accommodate over time changes in individual requirements and organisational demands.

## Responding to Change

Responsiveness to change is a more subtle, more qualitative aspect of building intelligence, the need for which is well illustrated by the Dutch management consultants', Twijnstra's, projection of the changing mission of the office building. In the sixties the design of office was influenced primarily by organisational efficiency (remember O & M studies, the endless arrays of elementary steel furniture, and the appearance of the office before carpet came into general use). In the seventies a new factor emerged which overtook but did not displace operational efficiency in office design - the need engendered by the energy crisis to cope with costs in use. Costs in Use in their turn have been overtaken in the eighties, but not removed, by a new wave of concern for office quality. Why this should happen just now is explained by the substantial changes in the structure of the office population brought by information technology - obedient, poorly paid clerks have been more or less replaced by better educated, more demanding, less easily satisfied professionals and managers who expect a better quality environment. Twijnstra argue that the office environment of the nineties will be influenced by yet another factor, the need to stimulate creativity, to galvanise inert office organisations into greater teamwork and more demanding intellectual effort. Architectural devices such as the atrium, which are often thought of simply as spatial gimickry, can alternatively be interpreted as a powerful means of making people in large organisations more aware of the totality of the organisation and the relationships between its pacts, ie. a means, if used correctly, of stimulating organisational change.

There is little evidence of such environmental ambitions in Japan. In fact the reality is that most Japanese offices are stuck firmly in the era of operational efficiency, the only interesting feature of which is the use of the office environment to emphasise collectivity and teamwork. However, it is also clear that the Japanese are less than happy with their existing offices. As one Japanese said to Professor Becker of Cornell, the pioneer of scientific Facilities Management, "Ten years ago your factories (American) were better than ours. Now ours are better equipped than yours. In ten years our offices will be better than yours".

In this sense, the Japanese are thus prepared to acknowledge what NTT omitted from its otherwise extremely comprehensive list of the features of the Intelligent Building - the fourth dimension of intelligence, the capacity to respond to new kinds of demand. Intelligent Buildings mean <u>Better</u> Buildings.

## Defining "Better" Buildings

"Better" is defined by the four kinds of intelligence described above. However, a word about buildings is necessary - they are not quite what they seem.

In a time of rapid organisational and technological change, buildings cannot continue to be regarded as large, heavy, permanent entities - slow to build and expensive to run. Office buildings, in particular, are contrived by the weaving together four major factors:

- information technology: the storage, processing, and transmittal of information, primarily by electronic media;

- organisation: the social structure which holds people together to carry out office tasks;

- building technology: the means available for constructing and servicing the building fabric;

- facilities management: the software by which the use of buildings is programmed and managed through time.

No one building is ideal for all organisations. Depending on each user's particular mix of information technology and organisational structure, entirely different kinds of building technology and facilities management will be required. For example, the contemporary Japanese and Swedish office buildings are totally different in appearance precisely because the office cultures of Japan and Sweden are so far apart. Such mixes change through time, never more so than at present, and to facilitate such change it is enormously helpful to look at office buildings not as complete entities but as a series of superimposed life cycles:

- the shell, skin, structure, designed customarily (although this is increasingly in question) to last for at least fifty years;

- the services, the primary mechanical and electrical systems which are increasingly important, and which have a life span usually no more than fifteen years;

- the scenery, the ceilings, partitions, furniture and finishes which constitute the fitting out which is necessary to accommodate a particular division or tenant.  Such elements are often cleared away within five to seven years of being installed, the customary length of a lease.

The more independent of each other these major time cycles are, the easier it is to change, for example, scenery without reconstructing the basic servicing structure or rebuilding the long term shell, the easier it is for a building to accommodate change.

Interest in different kinds of firms and different patterns in the use of building resource is not simply fascinating from a comparative anthropological point of view.  It is now of the utmost pragmatic importance in determining which building has the capacity (or the intelligence) to cope with different degrees of acceleration in organisational and technological change.  As the American psychologist, Kurt Lewin, once remarked, "There is nothing so practical as a good theory".

## The Development of Intelligent Buildings in North America

The most intensive discussion of Building Intelligence in North America has not been on Building Automation, although great advances have been made in energy management and in the development of automated building systems by firms such as Honeywell and Johnson Controls.  What has caught the headlines is the contribution of Office Automation & Advanced Telecommunications in the aggressive marketing of real estate.  The most common name for this is Shared Tenant Services, ie. value added by information technology services to multi-tenanted property.

There are three reasons for this characteristically North American emphasis on tenancy and service:

- the large scale and volatility of the North American real estate market and particularly the very important role of the speculative office developer.  While such developers exist in most European countries nowhere, except perhaps in the United Kingdom, is their importance so great;

- the excellent North American tradition of building management, the result of a buyers market and a much more responsive approach by landlords to tenants than exists, for example, in Britain.  The importance of building management is also obviously more important in a situation where office buildings tend to be much bigger than

in Europe and multi-tenancy is far more common.  It is also true
that US tenants are more mobile, more sophisticated and more
demanding.

- the deregulation of the great US telephone monopoly, the Bell
  System, which has introduced competition and a bewildering variety
  of choice for users of telecommunication services.  The legal
  reality is that not only is there competition between prime
  services but that each large building can, in effect, become a
  private utility company as far as telecommunications are
  concerned, run for the benefit of tenants and the profit of the
  landlord.

According to Harry D Levine, there were in the USA in mid-1985, the
height of the shared tenant services craze, approximately 100 office
projects to which shared tenant services were offered and several
hundred more under construction.  Most were large (over 50,000m$^2$),
high rise office buildings in major urban centres such as Houston,
Dallas and Atlanta, the cities which had been overbuilt since the 1982
recession and which exhibit high vacancy rates.  No one, according to
Levine, has yet become wealthy through providing shared tenant
services and there is considerable doubt about the profitability of
some already installed.  There have been some notable failures and a
gradual realisation not only that some tenants resist the concept of
sharing (they have their own preferred systems) but also that the
management of shared tenant services is a considerable and labour
intensive necessity.  The movement tends to be vendor driven - a
combination of anxious developers and eager telecoms salesmen - and
there is little evidence of a grand swell of demand from critical end
users.  However, recently the most active of the associations which
have grown in this field, the International Intelligent Building
Association, seems to be moving in a consumerist direction.

To Europeans, used to monopolistic and slow moving PTTs and very often
to custom built office buildings, the amount of type has been
astonishing.  Nevertheless it is quite clear that shared tenant
services are likely to survive as a long term concept.  In cities such
as Dallas STS has become a feature which no premier office development
can be without.  The chief achievement is a product of the integrating
culture of the communications age - the linking of two entities which
previously had been conceptually quite distinct, real estate and
telecommunications.

Japanese Developments in Building Intelligence

Attention has already been drawn to the extremely comprehensive
presentation by NTT of building intelligence.  There is considerable
interest in Japan in what intelligence means for building design.  At
least one of the three factors which explain the rise of the
intelligent building in the USA exists in Japan - the deregulation of
the telephone monopoly, NTT in late 1986.

The paradoxical context is a society which is dependent on trading in high tech products which is yet using them as extensively as many firms in North America and Western Europe; a stock of office space in Tokyo, for example, which includes some advanced buildings but many others of poor quality, which are at least as vulnerable to obsolescence caused by information technology as those in Britain; as well as generally conservative and labour intensive forms of office organisation which are nonetheless extremely effective.

What strikes the outsider as different to Europe or North America is:

- the vision, expressed frequently in brochures and publicity, of while organisations (eg. Toshiba) not just as a collection of semi autonomous units, nor as organisation charts which stress control and power, but as interactive networks of communications, which overcome geographical dispersal and divisional specialisation.

- the concreteness of the idea of the intelligent building as a product or a series of products, quite different from the American emphasis on marketing, and much more precise than European equivocation. Behind the obvious commercial motives, there seems to be for the Japanese a drive towards an aesthetic of complete electronic capability;

- a willingness to extend the idea of the intelligent building beyond the isolated site, beyond the particular organisation, to a much large scale. A new kind of City planning is seen to be a logical extension of the intelligent building - hence plans for Tokyo Bay, for the Osaka Teleport, and for the competition for the City of Kawasaki: "Kawasaki as an Advanced Information City", in which electronics turns the city into a gigantic, continuous, university level seminar.

Given the close knit structure of Japanese industry, and the ability of the great trading houses to take ideas and turn them into products, it is not too fanciful to anticipate that the Japanese will succeed in exploiting Building Intelligence firstly to regenerate their decaying city fabrics, which are suffering from the relative decline of the old capital industries, and secondly to capture a vast potential market for a new generation of products based on building intelligence, such as superior lifts, air conditioning units, and office furniture.

The European Contribution

European offices, particularly those in Scandinavia, Germany and Holland have developed in a quite different way to those in North America and Japan. The difference is not so much technological as organisational, and is due in particular to the enormous influence of widespread industrial democracy on the quality of working life.

Because Northern European offices tend to be custom built and because consultation between employers and employees about the office environment is so common, the Northern European office has taken a dramatic step away from the big open plan towards highly individualised, cellular offices in which the need to give direct aspect to nature is the strongest determinant of form.

Consequently the new generation low rise, cellular, finger like offices in Northern Europe is quite unlike those found anywhere else in the world.

In this the developer has played an insignificant role.  The PTTs themselves are making slow progress towards deregulation so that the duopoly in the UK between BT and Mercury is liberal by European standards.  What influence has the intelligent building had?

There are three:

- Building intelligence has been linked, as in Japan, very firmly to large scale economic planning and redevelopment.  Examples include the use of Advanced Telecommunications (Wide Area Networks and the like) to provide a locational edge for developments like the Amsterdam & Koln teleports, for whole cities like Milton Keynes, for areas of urban regeneration like London Docklands.  Much more than in the USA and Japan the teleport movement is itself a covert step towards deregulation of the PTTs, by providing for the first time on a large scale competitive pricing for telecommunications services.

- The use of Building Automation, not just at whole building level such as the design of energy efficient perimeter skin walls or all comprehending security systems, but at the micro level of the workstations, allowing each individual office worker to adjust lighting, air conditioning, and access to data.

- A significant contribution, at least as important as that in the United States and far more advanced than that of Japan, in thinking about how buildings can be made more responsive to change.  This contribution has largely been in inventing ways of measuring building performance on a rigorous, comparative basis.

Building Evaluation

Measuring building performance is one aspect of the increasingly important software of Facilities Management.  It depends upon powerful, well organised users who are anxious to achieve buildings which meet their changing demands over time.

Facilities Management, which developed first in the United States, has been given an enormous boost by the take up of information technology in the office. The office has become, in effect, an adjacent to the computer and, as a result, the importance of the building as a means of achieving organisational success has been enormously enhanced.

The ORBIT 1 study, carried out by DEGW, Building Use Studies and EOSYS in the United Kingdom in 1982/3, established design criteria for offices in the era of information technology. ORBIT 2 (DEGW, Harbinger, and Professor Sims and Becker from Cornell University, 1985) developed these criteria in the quite different context of North America into a technique for aiding building users and developers to assess how demand for office space by different kinds of office organisations with different kinds of technology was changing. In addition the ORBIT 2 technique allows the same users and developers to measure supply in terms of the capacity to accommodate changing organisational and technological demands of any given building. The method can be applied at the level of an individual building, the stock of space held by an organisation or existing in a city, and related to the needs of divisions, organisations, of whole sections of the office market.

In terms of Building Intelligence this is the most important task - linking supply with demand. No building, however automated, with whatever enhancement of office automation or advanced telecommunications, is intelligent unless it can cope with change. Such measurements as those in ORBIT 2 are the first real tests of that intelligence. ORBIT 2 completes the loop between building hardware and software, and brings the four factors mentioned at the beginning - information technology, organisation, building technology, and facilities management, into one complete system.

The City of the Twenty First Century

In the course of the completion of ORBIT 1, a prediction was made, rather rashly it seemed at the time. This was that the introduction of information technology into office buildings built in the British office boom of the sixties and early seventies, would be so demanding and stressful that for many users their existing office stock would become prematurely obsolete. What premature obsolescence means is quite precise: the moment when the cost of bringing an office building up to date to meet the new demands of emerging information technology exceeds the cost of tearing the building down and beginning again.

The prediction has come true in London with a force that was not anticipated. Never before famous for architectural innovation, the City of London is today a remarkable proof of how closely architectural form is linked to social and technological change.

The ostensible cause is "Big Bang", the deregulation on October 27, 1986 of the Stock Exchange. Underneath lie the internationalisation of the financial services industry and the concentration in a limited number of world cities, of which London is one, of unprecedented concentrations of telecommunications and computing power. The result is huge pressure on the existing office stock, rendered as predicted prematurely obsolete. The inevitable consequence is a rapid programme of construction of a new generation of office buildings, of a far superior order to those they replace. Office buildings of the sixties are being torn down to make way for the new. The whole pattern of property values is shifting as existing space in traditional locations is usable to compete with new space of the new quality.

The prototype of the new kind of office is Richard Rogers new building for the Corporation of Lloyds - a building which contradicts most of the traditional rules of office development. Needless to say it exhibits all four dimensions of building intelligence:

- Office Automation
- Advanced Telecommunications
- Building Automation
- Responsiveness to Change

Because of excellent briefing, and the peculiar needs of the Corporation of Lloyds (a market place in which shared information for member firms is critical) Lloyd's is London's first Intelligent Office building and it is, no doubt, the precursor of many more.

Tom Cross, author of Intelligent Buildings, says (from an obviously American marketing perspective) that the intelligent building is the one that is fully let. To his basic definition the Japanese would add a dimension of technological completeness and the Europeans one of responsiveness to individual needs and organisational change.

We have a long way to go before the perfect building, whether in Japan, the USA or in Europe meets the completely satisfied user. Nevertheless, it should be clear that the challenge ahead is at least the equivalent to the invention of the office building in Chicago one hundred years ago, when a new office technology of typewriter and telephones was necessary to open up the Midwest. What faces us today is not only the invention of a new kind of office but also the City of the Twenty First Century.

# Buildings for business: the customer's view

PETER PORTLOCK
REGIONAL PROPERTY OPERATIONS MANAGER - SOUTH
IBM UNITED KINGDOM LIMITED

A commercial building occupier is not generally interested in whether his building is High Tech, Low Tech, or Tech at all.  What he wants is to be able to run his business successfully and effectively.  His main focus is to minimise his capital investment and operating costs, maximise his ability to attract and keep good staff and provide the best possible, most competitive service to his customers.

This paper will seek to explore and examine these focus areas, attempt to define the basic occupier's requirements, and seek to identify how these requirements are likely to change through time.

Peter Portlock is the Regional Property Operations Manager - South for IBM in the UK, having responsibility for design, construction, operation and maintenance activities over a portfolio of 1.2 million square feet.  He joined IBM 13 years ago with a degree in building engineering and a doctorate in computer-aided building design.

Presented at HIGH-TECH BUILDINGS 87: Online Publications, Pinner, UK, 1987

High Tech - Who needs it?

Technology when applied to the building process, the operation of buildings or the functions that go on in them, is only a means to an end and not an end in itself.  Switching your individual office lights on by dialling the building computer on your telephone is clearly wizardry of the most elegant kind, but it is difficult at first sight to see the benefits this has over a wall switch.

The client comes at the whole business of technology from a totally different direction from the engineer, designer or developer.  He has only one question - "Will it make my business more successful?"; if the answer is "no" or "probably not" then, unless there is some separate corporate image or identity reason for appearing to be up to date, his attention will shift to something that will.

The contribution that buildings and their services make to business success is the acid test.  Success in business is about minimising capital and operating cost investment, while providing the best and most competitive service to the customer.  This success is sustained by ensuring that the best staff are attracted and retained and proper attention is paid to long-term planning.

So clients or occupiers don't want High Tech buildings.  They want buildings that work for them, protecting the activity, supporting business goals and projecting the company.  At the same time they look for an ability to continue to cope and operate effectively as needs change and develop.

In attempting to provide buildings for the lease holder or owner - occupier market, the building design criteria must then clearly be linked with the needs and objectives of the client.

Buildings - They need to be ready

Once set the structural elements of buildings don't, or rarely, get changed.  Thus, a building designed without proper thought will be a drag on business effectiveness for years.  The three areas to be considered are:

- Space
- Dimension
- Capacity

and the design thinking must be geared to making notional provision for change and development.

. Space

Here we are talking about the general provision of space in the service areas of a building:

- Is there sufficient space in the plant rooms to add more boiler, chiller, transformer capacity?

- Can goods and equipment get in through goods in?

. Dimension

Structural dimensions are a significant constraint in many buildings.

- Does the clear slab to slab dimension allow for the provision of a raised floor and/or a suspended ceiling?

- Does the distance between columns and their disposition allow full utilisation of available space?

- Does the module make for sensible compartmentation of the floor space?

- Can big pieces of equipment (copiers, filing cupboards, computers) be got into and out of the lift?

. Capacity

Three elements of structural capacity are important.

- Are the floor loadings sufficient to take modern office equipment <u>in any location</u>?

- Is the roof loading sufficient to cope with additional roof plant/tanks?

- Is the capacity of service riser ducts enough for about double the anticipated maximum need?

These structural requirements are easy to overlook or prune but deficiencies are generally extremely costly and disruptive to remedy, or work around. Getting these things right doesn't make a building High Tech. However, it means that the client has a good chance of being able to meet his changing needs over time effectively and economically.

## Building Services - The same story

Whereas the building structure, once provided, is generally a fix for the life of the building, the utilities and services to and in a building are likely to be upgraded or replaced several times. To avoid early obsolescence or disruptive modifications, however, again it is important to make the correct initial provision both in terms of the services running to a building and the services capacity and distribution within a building.

. Service incomers

   Supporting the needs of modern business activities puts increasingly heavy demands on utility services. Generally two considerations are important:

   - Is sufficient electrical power provided to the building to cater for both building and business equipment loads?

   - Is the provision or availability of BT and other communication networks adequate for current and likely future needs?

. Internal Service Provision and Distribution

   The most important element at the beginning of a building facility provision project is to establish a servicing strategy. That means providing answers to the questions:

   - How much of each service do I need to provide by when?

   - How do I get it to where I am likely to need it?

   - How do I avoid having a problem if my requirements change?

Answers to these basic servicing questions are often provided in extremely complex technical terms. The answers also frequently revolve around the provision of significant day one flexibility and over-capacity. Unfortunately that's not what the simple user/client wants. What he wants is a strategy that enables him to go step by step from where he is today to where he wants to get to.

## What about the Workers?

Today as never before the success of a business or enterprise is determined by the effectiveness and productivity of the people working within the organisation. Although, clearly, management systems, organisations, policies and procedures operate independently of the physical environment within a building, the building, the facilities it offers and the environment it provides, all have a big part to play in the productivity and motivation of those working there.

As far as people are concerned, any organisation aims to get and to keep the best staff it can, and to maximise their abilities and output to the organisation's benefit. The most successful organisations pursue this aim by attempting to combine an obvious, effectiveness-orientated modern image, the provision of real support to productive working and a visible and real consideration of and attention to employees' needs and well-being.

So how are buildings involved? They are involved a lot. A whole host of building-related factors have to be considered in determining what must be achieved to give the employee the most effective support to do his job and to keep him motivated.

By considering buildings as cost centres and their occupants as profit generators, we can begin to take a user's view and take account of the needs of the individual in the earliest stages of building and interior design. The objective is to maximise the employee's profit-generating potential at minimum cost; but to achieve that objective today means that we have to start to question some of the accepted design philosophy developed over the last ten years.

## The Workstation - Where the work gets done

The development of electronic office systems offers the opportunity to deliver to the individual workstation great productivity both in terms of computer power and facility for communication. As organisations and individuals switch dependency from paper and face-to-face contact to remote, paperless, electronic operation, the design thinking for office space has to be adjusted to take account of this new man/office hardware relationship - adjusted for the requirements of the machine and adjusted for the effect on the person.

In considering this relationship the differences between the parties are important.

1.  People are interesting and require stimulation - machines are not and do not.

2.  People's needs change - a machine's needs remain constant.

3.  People's effectiveness is subject to environmental influence - a machine's effectiveness generally isn't.

From a user's viewpoint the "building" has to support the needs of both employees and machines and help the relationship to work. A user must, therefore, consider a building or fit-up design with the following in mind:

.  Machine needs

  -  Can I get sufficient connection to each workstation in terms of power, data cabling and BT?

  -  Can the HVAC system hold the temperature within the required operating band?

.  People needs

  -  Can the individual exercise sufficient local control in terms of temperature, lighting and glare levels to allow him to do his work most effectively?

  -  Is the space such as to give sufficient aural and visual protection to individuals?

  -  Is the furniture right for the job and does it integrate with the overall design concept?

These questions are simple to put but answers can combine to produce potentially wasteful and expensive solutions.

## Operating Cost - Where profit is dissipated

The cost of running buildings is made up of four components, fixed charges, maintenance, energy/utilities and manpower. This is all overhead to the business and as such generates little enthusiasm in a building user whose interest is to spend a minimum consistent with the achievement of his business objectives. Fixed charges such as rent, rates and depreciation are little influenced by building form or technology but in the other areas several points are important:

  -  Maintenance

    .  Is the fabric low maintenance and of credible design?
    .  Are the service and utilities systems simple and accessible?

  -  Energy/Utilities

    .  Are all incoming services properly metered?
    .  Is there sufficient and effective control over the lighting and HVAC systems?

.   Has the building energy balance equation been properly
    evaluated?

-   Manpower

    Can the building accept automated or electronic systems to
    handle, for example, security or fire protection, that
    would result in a reduction of building operating staff?

A proper consideration of these points can result in real money
savings to a building occupier - and that is very important to him.

So what are the answers?

Building users do not know all the answers, but increasingly they do
know the right questions to ask.  It is the job of the building
providers to fully research and understand the user needs and provide
facilities that meet the requirements.  Failure to do this results in
unlet buildings and unhappy owner occupiers.

Some general trends and guidelines are apparent.

The amount of business support technology in buildings is growing and
will continue to do so.  Buildings need, therefore, to be designed to
handle this and this generally means being designed with the ability
to cope with growth; growth of the loads on the structure, growth of
the loads on the services and utilities systems, growth of the amount
of data, power and BT cabling in the riser and trunking distribution
systems.

The impact of technology on the operational effectiveness within
buildings has other influences on building design.  The focus on the
individual and the type of work he has to do tends to generate a need
for more highly cellular, individually controllable areas.  This
suggests a move away from deep plan, highly serviced, flexible space
towards shallow space of a fairly simple and rigid concept with
simple servicing and service distribution systems offering
flexibility at the workstation rather than within the building
infrastructure.

Finally the positive effect that the incorporation of advances in
technology can have on the operational efficiency of the building
itself must not be ignored.  To go back to the example at the
beginning of this paper, it may well be an indulgence to have a
computer switch on your lights in response to a phone call: however,
a computer that switches off your lights when you've gone home could
be a sensible business investment.

# Wills & ways: how high-tech users can survive & succeed in low-tech buildings

Robert   Fernandez
Property Director
Manufacturers Hanover
England

The dealer is one of the most intensive users of new
technology.  Buildings which are purpose designed to
meet the needs of such users are now available.  But the
majority of buildings in the City were designed for an
entirely different operation.  Will the institutions who
occupy such buildings be able to survive as they
introduce more and more technology?  Recently
Manufacturers Hanover installed a 34 position dealing
room in its 60's design H.Q. building in the City.  The
lessons learned indicate that the high tech user can
survive and succeed in low tech buildings, but only
under certain conditions .......

Robert Fernandez is Property
Director for Manufacturers
Hanover.  He is responsible for
Property management of all their
U.K. buildings - totalling some
500,000 square feet.  A Founder
Fellow and Council member of the
Association of Facilities
Managers, he has been engaged in
property related activities for
nearly 20 years.

Presented at HIGH-TECH BUILDINGS 87: Online Publications, Pinner, UK, 1987

## The Dealer - User of New Technology

The dealer is one of the most intensive users of new technology in the modern office.

The job involves the use of:

- financial market information systems
- voice and data telecommunications
- in-house deal processing systems

In turn these systems require:

- vast quantitites of cabling
- increased electric power

The heat loads created by these systems need to be dissipated.

Because of the investment in hardware and people, Uninterruptible Power Supply equipment and Emergency Power Generators are used to maintain integrity of power supplies to avoid interruptions to the operation.

These factors impose considerable strains on all but the most recent buildings.

## High-Tech Buildings

Buildings are now being designed and built with the needs of such new technology users in mind.

The height from structural slab to structural slab is sufficient to provide:

- raised floor voids which can accommodate power, voice and data cabling,
- air conditioning equipment within suspended ceiling void,
- an acceptable head height in the occupied area between.

Risers, sufficient for the vertical distribution of power, voice and data cabling are provided.

Base building air conditioning plant is designed to cope with the heat loads of the modern office without recourse to supplementary systems.

Power supplies are adequate for all needs.

If not supplied with the building, provision is made to accommodate Emergency Power Generators.

## High Tech Users in Low Tech Buildings

Those institutions which have the most accute need have already moved, or are planning to move into such buildings. But most City based institutions occupy buildings which are not "high tech". Can such institutions survive in these buildings as they install more and more new technology?

The answer is that they can survive and succeed but only subject to specific conditions.

These conditions were identified when Manufacturers Hanover recently undertook the installation of a new dealing room in its HQ building in the City of London.

## The Building

The building is a late 1960's design, was constructed in 1970 and 1971 and was first occupied in 1972.

It has offices on ground and 7 upper floors, a basement which is the staff dining room and a sub basement which is occupied mainly by plant and storage.

Each upper floor is approximately 5,000 ft$^2$. The dealing room as extended now occupies 4,000 ft$^2$.

The slab to slab height is typically 9'0".

The house air conditioning has central plant with air being delivered to the offices via perimeter induction units. The system is barely able to cope in areas where there are normal heat loads. Wherever significant increased heat loads have occurred, supplementary air conditioning has had to be provided.

The building is served by two vertical distribution risers. Both are small and have been virtually full for some years. One is adjacent to the offices and connects easily to the horizontal under floor trunking distribution system. Access from the other to the office floor is by a tortuous route which makes additional cabling from the riser to the office space a nightmare.

There are 2 generators, one handling essential house services the other available for priority equipment e.g. telephone system.

Neither can be easily upgraded. The building has no oil tank. Oil supplies have to be brought in by barrel.

## Case Study

Installation of a 34 position dealing room with all new equipment and environment in the space occupied by an existing dealing room.

## In-House Project Team

The in-house project team consisted of 3 members.

-    The Foreign Exchange Dealer manager who was User Representative and overall co-ordinator.
-    A Communications manager who dealt with all the communications and other systems.
-    A Facilities Manager who arranged the design and construction aspects of the Project.

## The Professional Team

The Thomas Saunders Partnership were appointed as Space Planners and Interior Designers.

They were selected because they had done good work for Manufacturers Hanover previously. Besides they had just completed a similar project for a competitor!

## Phasing

Because there was very little free space on the floor, it was necessary to tackle the work in phases.

When the first phase was complete, the dealers were moved into the new area and the space vacated by them became the next phase.

The co-ordination necessary to achieve this with no interruption to service was only possible by having a small tightly knit project team.

## Desk Design

Each desk position was provided with:

- a new dealerboard (1 screen)
- market information services (2 screens)
- voice communication systems
- in-house deal processing system (1 screen, 1 digipad, 1 personal computer)

Because each dealing position had to accommodate this equipment, a much bigger work station was required. Full consultation at every stage of development - and eventually a full size mock-up for testing by the dealers - ensured no surprises on the day they moved in.

## Power

The increased power needs all but used up the remaining spare capacity on the incoming mains supply.

## UPS

Spare capacity on an existing UPS did not provide total coverage for all the new equipment. In consultation with the dealers only the key positions were included on the UPS supply.

## EPG

Spare capacity on an existing EPG provided coverage for all the new systems. Only the supplementary air conditioning in the dealing room could not be included on the EPG supply.

## Air Conditioning

The equipment on each desk produced heat loads which the house system could not cope with. A supplementary air conditioning system was installed with chilled air being delivered via the suspended ceiling void.

## Raised Floor

The existing dealing room had a 6" raised floor (which provided a 4" void). Despite the vast increase in the number of cables the relatively shallow void was sufficient.

- Cables were introduced into the void at 3 different points.

- Cables were spread out under the raised floor via an extensive tray grid.

## Slab to Slab Height

The slab to slab height on this floor was 9'0". the suspended ceiling void was 1'0". The raised floor was 6". The height between raised floor surface and suspended ceiling was thus reduced to 7'6"!

## Lighting

The lighting required by the dealers had to throw light onto the desk surface but had to cause no glare on the screens.   The right effect was achieved by a process of trial and error using a full scale mock-up.

## Ceiling

The ceiling was replaced by a lay-in tile system which gave full and easy access to the ceiling void for maintenance of the air conditioning and lighting.

## New Equipment Room

To avoid using prime office space for equipment, an equipment room was constructed in the sub basement.

Providing chilling for the equipment in this room was only possible because of in-house engineers familiarity with the building.  They identified a circuitous route for the coolant piping from the room to the compressors 3 floors above.

## New Riser

The existing building riser was full. Using the new equipment room was only possible by finding a new way of running cables from that room to the dealing room.  At this point the Architect earned his fee.  His eagerly adopted suggestion was to convert an adjacent stairwell into a cable riser.

## Conclusion

Manufacturers Hanover were successful in installing their new dealing room in their low tech building but it required:

### Creativity:

-   in evolving the right structure and composition of its in-house project team
-   in finding a route for coolant piping from sub basement to compressors
-   in constructing a new riser in the stairwell

### Communication:

-   to ensure that the dealers were fully committed to the success of the project
-   to ensure that the efforts of the Construction Contractor and the many systems vendors were totally co-ordinated

### Compromise:

-   the 12" ceiling void was barely adequate for the supplementary air conditioning trunking
-   a deeper raised floor void would have simplified cable installation
-   the 7'6" headroom was acceptable only because of the relatively small area of the dealing room
-   not all desk positions could be included on UPS
-   the EPG was unable to cater for the supplementary air conditioning

### Survival and Success

The project was completed on time and under budget. Negative feedback has been minimal. Since completion the number of positions has been increased up to maximum capacity. Foreign Exchange profits are reported to be buoyant!

Determined, Resourceful, Imaginative High Tech users can survive and succeed in low tech buildings.

But, experience should teach them what kind of buildings they should be specifying and demanding from the Building supply Industry.

# Integrated building communications:
# a tenant's dream or an owner's nightmare

Stephen J. Baker
Senior Consultant
Systems Designers plc
England

Voice and data communications requirements are reaching new demands, particularly in the financial sector. Demands, not only upon the cabling infrastructure but also other building services and technical staff. These are resulting in opportunities for providing a centrally developed and managed communications facility. It is the ascertion of this paper that such a facility can be provided and in a way that has tangible benefits for both tenant and building owner.

Stephen Baker is a Senior Consultant with over eighteen years experience of computer and communications development. At present he is developing his company's contribution to a consortium of companies, to realise the potential building communications market.
Systems Designers plc is a leading European consultancy and software house with over 1500 staff located in the UK, Europe and North America.

Presented at HIGH-TECH BUILDINGS 87: Online Publications, Pinner, UK, 1987

## 1.    INTRODUCTION

The integration of building communications, through a centrally developed and managed service, is a solution that will prove beneficial to the tenant and a marketable asset to the building owner.

Telecommunications within a building, particularly a multi-tenanted office block, has always been seen as being the responsibility of the individual tenant. This practice has operated, since telecommunications first began, with fairly simple and straight-forward telephones and, perhaps, telex. Since the advent of computers and, in particular, on-line systems the increase of terminals has placed additional strains upon building services. The enhancements of these computer systems has tended to proceed without much reference to the other building services, with the all too common result of conflict occuring between the building owner and the tenant. Services such as cable ducting, cooling, heating and lighting have all been subjected to uncoordinated and irrational change that has resulted in frustration and conflict between tenant and building owner. Uncomfortable working conditions for the employees has been a major problem.

These factors, plus others, are making demands upon the tenant that are either too costly for him to meeet or are beyond his technical ability to either plan for or implement. The time is now ripe for new initiatives to be introduced and for which technology can begin to supply solutions.

Before discussing a viable solution, it is essential to identify the requirements that have led to this belief.

## 2.    THE REQUIREMENTS

It has already been stated that communication, both within a building and as an interface to outside services, has long been the responsibility of the tenant. Large sums of capital have been tied up in unplanned and mis-managed cabling systems, to the extent that it is cheaper and less disruptive not to take out redundant cables, This, coupled with inadequate cable ducts, has proved a source of conflict between the tenant and the building owner, particularly when the tenancy is vacated. As more equipment is added to the office or its positioning changed, the effects upon the other building services can be quite dramatic. Again it is usually the tenants responsibility to plan and co-ordinate, providing he has taken into consideration these other services. With relatively simple requirements, these activities are coped with. However, many systems now have a direct impact upon the business they support, and their reliability and availability depends as much upon the success of the other building services as on the integrity of the system itself. The emergence of Dealing Room systems has shown just how close these services are now intertwined.

The complexity of today's business systems has grown because of the insatiable need for information. New services are being offered by Value Added Service providers that enable even the smallest company to be in touch with world-wide information systems. A comprehensive and sophisticate information strategy can give a company a tremendous edge over its competitors. However, to plan, develop and manage such a system requires on-site specialists who can provide day to day management. These specialists are usually employed by the tenant to manage the facility but demand for their services is far out stripping supply which, has not only produced a dearth of competent staff, but has fuelled a salary explosion. The staff costs involved in maintaining a small network, twelve hours a day can be well in excess of £70,000 per annum just for one tenant. In addition to staff costs economies of scale, either for services or products, are heavily weighed against a small tenant.

The "requirement" can be encapsulated in the proposition that communications facilities should be a centrally provided utility for which the tenant pays both a premium on rental charges plus "as used" costs. The infrastructure of cabling and interface products (PABX, telex, facsimile, data communications, video, telementary etc) should be of no more concern to the tenant than, say, heating, lighting, security, cleaning etc. It can be argued that the provision of a communications system is at a "higher level", than the other services mentioned. However, just as these other services can be offered by specialist companies, so too can the provision and on-going management of communications systems. In fact it can be taken further by saying that with the provision of a centralised system the following requirements can be satisfied:

a)   A centrally managed system available to all tenants.
b)   Quantifiable benefits.
c)   Economies of scale.
d)   Better use of resources, technology and staff.
e)   More flexible system with realistic fall-back.
f)   Easier problem accountability.
g)   Strategic development of the communications
     infrastructure and its services and products.

However, whilst these may be the points a tenant is looking for, the provision of them, by the building owner and in a way that is commercially and financially acceptable, is one that requires careful thought.

There are, basically, four technologies that need to be considered:

2.1   Cabling Infrastructure
           Often termed Local Area Network (LAN)

2.2   Voice Technolgy
           PABX, paging etc

2.3   Data Technology
           Terminals, comms. engines, databases etc

2.4   Video Technolgy
           Security, conferencing, training etc.


2.1   **CABLING INFRASTRUCTURE**

Within any building, cabling for voice, data and telementary systems is a requirement that will only get worse. One answer is to make ducting so large, in anticipation of expansion, that flexibility is lost and valuable space is taken up incorporating these structures. Another, probably more practical solution, is to provide cable that thas vast quantities of capacity but cuts down upon congestion caused by multi-cables. However, it is necessary that initial building design incorporates the virues of this type of cable and the advantages that a designed cable management system gives. The design of this system would be capable of having pragmatic contingency and fall-back elements built-in, that could then incorporate critical telementary systems.

## 2.2    VOICE TECHNOLOGY

Voice technology is mainly served through the provision of Private Automatic Branch Exchange (PABX) and appropriate handsets. A large centrally provided and staffed PABX will enable a range of functionality and flexibility not usually available on either "key phones" or small PABX. Through the use of software, new services can be developed for the tenant which will provide better management information for call-loging and cost allocation. Voice mailbox and message desk handling will also be an attractive proposition.

## 2.3    DATA TECHNOLOGY

Data technology has a variety of components ranging from terminals (ie visual display units, printers, facsimile, telex etc), through the different cabling techniques to the interface equipment, that enables connections to be made to external services. The progress being made by manufacturers and Value Added Service providers, presents a considerable problem to tenants as they seek to take advantage of these services in a cost effective way. Sharing these services, on a centrally provided basis, will enable not only considerable savings but provide for more sophisticated functionality.

The sharing of such services as packet switching, telex, teletex, facsimile and even satellite dish all become more realistic for an individual tenant to use.

## 2.4    VIDEO TECHNOLOGY

Video technology has been relatively slow to provide applications that are appealing and cost effective to the majority of tenants. Slow-scan video, for use in security surveillance, is probably the one application of regular use and acceptance. However, video conferencing has not proved so successful for a number of reasons, which include cost effectiveness and convenience. This latter point is particularly true if the studio is some distance from the tenants office. A centrally provided studio, perhaps serving a number of buildings, may prove more successful.

3.     **THE OPPORTUNITY**

With the availability of a communications facility, which is centrally designed, installed, managed and developed, the tenant will enjoy a number of benefits that he should be encouraged to take into consideration when comparing buildings. Similarly, these benefits can be used as a marketing edge by the building owner.

Benefits to a tenant will include:

a)     Better economise of scale.

b)     More effective management and control.

c)     More effective problem detection and resolution.

d)     Better coordinated and predictable "change" management.

e)     Pragmatic provision of fall-back and contingency.

f)     Easier and cost effective provision of external services.

g)     Less or no technical staff required.

h)     No capital tied up in cabling, control and monitoring equipment or equipment that would prove unsuitable at a new premises.

The building owner would benefit from:

a)     A marketable building asset.

b)     Controlled development of other building services, affected by communications expansion (e.g. lighting, heating, cooling, ducting etc).

c)     A re-usable asset, from one tenant occupancy to another.

d)     A fully integrated building management service, with the communications requirement as the prime reference point for the other services.

e)     The opportunity to provide revenue earning Value Added Services.

f)     Being able to attract the type of tenant who will be willing to pay a premium for the use of such facilities.

## 4.     THE SOLUTION

Whilst it is important that a "need" can be identified and that suitable products are available, it is essential that a pragmatic integration path is developed.

Within the communications industry there are two important developments, that have internationally recognised standards associated with them.     The first is "Open Systems Interconnection" (OSI), which allows for hardware and software development to be conducted in a way that enables compatibility between systems.     The second is "Integrated Services Digital Network" (ISDN), which will allow integration of voice and data services through common servers.     OSI will allow application and equipment connection and ISDN will act as an integrated transport mechanism for voice and data.

As these standards are continually being developed and enhanced, full implementation is not yet with us.     However, sufficient products are available that provide an opportunity to bring the concept to the market place, without compromising the quality of service offered or its "managability".


### 4.1     CABLING

Cabling systems, in particular fibre optics, are now available that allow numerous systems to physically share the cable whilst remaining logically separate.     This is important whilst products are being used that do not conform to OSI or ISDN standards.     The large capacity of fibre optics makes co-existance over a single cable feasible.     With the high "band-width" available to fibre optic cables, the number of individual cables required, compared with co-axial or twisted-pair, is greatly reduced.     Security and integrity of data is greatly enhanced and co-existence with mains cables, lighting fitting and electro-magnetic equipment is overcome. In addition, duct space savings on individual floors, and space savings within risers should be considerable.

## 4.2   VOICE

A shared PABX, located and staffed centrally, would be feasible using an appropriately designed cabling system. However, additional benefits could accrue through centralised staffing of the PABX for call answering and distribution, although individual tenant identification can be retained when answering incoming calls. Call management facilities would be more cost effective and sophisticated charge allocation and tenant management information more readily available. A number of additional Value Added Services such as Voice Mailbox, message desk, security access control, "least cost" routing etc, all become pratical when shared.

Telephone handsets could be provided either as a standard item or, if required by an individual tenant, particular feature phones or attachments could be added.

There are companies that produce ISDN compatible PABX that will interface with ISDN exchanges as and when the PTT's begin introducing the service.

## 4.3   DATA

As with the PABX, data products can take advantage of the cabling system by providing centrally managed facilities. Terminals would be located at their point of use or, if appropriate, on a shared bureau basis. However, interfaces with external services could all be located in a conveniently managed area. Terminals, such as VDU's personnal computers, printers, telex machines, facsimile machines and other types of equipment, could be added to the cabling system in a way that not only ensured attachment compatibility but would be switchable to a number of different services and servers. Equipment, interfacing to external services, particularly packet switching servers, telex and facsimile store and forward and protocol convertors, would allow a wide range of applications to be made available.

The provision of these services would also be much quicker, particularly if already used by other tenants. In many cases services such as financial databases, access to host computers for booking services, information retrieval could all be existing and supplied by VAN providers. However, others could come equally from the building communication's system and could include mailbox, telex relay, information broadcast etc.

## 4.4   VIDEO

The benefits of a centrally provided video system may take some time to justify, however for those tenants whose needs for video conferencing can be shared with others, new applications may develop.

## 5.   MARKET SECTOR

The benefits of a centrally provided, integrated building communciations strategy, will differ between building type and profile of tenant. Needless to say, the concept is adaptable to any situation, providing it can be justified. The concerns of the "building" will mainly reflect the cabling design and management whereas choice of application's hardware and software will reflect tenant profiles.

## 5.1   NEW AND EXISTING BUILDINGS

The main concern is the ability to successfully install and maintain a cabling system and have adequate support services (heating, lighting, cooling etc) available.

Providing consultation is performed at an early enough stage, within the design of a building, there is an opportunity for the architect to take into consideration voice and data cabling requirements. With a suitably designed ducting system "fire-break" integrity is less likely to be compromised, by tenants drilling new routes.

Existing buildings, particularly those designed in the 1960's and 1970's will have accute, but not impossible, problems. Of particular concern here will be the adequacy of floor to ceiling heights and the ability of the support services to cope with the higher terminal population. A detailed study would be made to ascertain the work required to bring the existing services to an appropriate level of acceptability.

## 5.2    PRE-LET AND SPECULATIVE

Even with a cabling system in place, the provision of PABX and data communications facilities must be flexible enough to cater for many types of tenant profiles. Pre-let buildings offer the best opportunity of matching functionality with tenant profiles. However, the objective is to install flexible and re-usable products therefore the challenge of a speculative let need not be dismissed out of hand.

## 5.3    SINGLE TENANTED AND MULTI-TENANTED

The concept is appropriate to both, however, the multi-tenanted building would reap the majority of benefits, for both the tenant and the owner.

## 5.4    TENANT PROFILES

It is not necessary to have a detailed requirements specification, of each tenant, before knowing whether the facilities offered will be suitable. However, potential tenants can be grouped into profiles that will contain requirements that are common. Some of these profiles would include:

-    Financial services
-    Banking
-    Corporate head office
-    Consumer services

etc etc.

By understanding which profile a tenant belongs to, a suitable "package" can be devised. This categorisation could also be used to target a specific area. For instance; the City of London would tend to have financial services, banking and corporate head offices as predominant profiles.

From the above Market Sector categories, various scenarios can be built up to demonstrate risk and return.

The best scenario, from an implementation point of view, would be:

-    New building
-    Pre-let
-    Single-tenant.

To maximise return, the scenario might be:

-    New building
-    Pre-let
-    Multi-tenanted
-    Common profile.

From a maximum risk, point of view, it may be:

-    Existing building
-    Speculative
-    Multi-tenanted
-    Diverse profiles.

Even with a "maximum" risk building, a premium can be put onto the rental to cover that risk.


## 6.    REALISING THE CONCEPT

If the concept makes commercial sense, how can it be brought to the market place? There are two ways:

-    The building owner does it himself.
-    A specialist company is brought in.

For the purposes of this paper and some of the points already made, it is assumed that the building owner would not wish to take direct responsibility. But, if a specialist is brought in, does that mean dealing with yet another company? A solution is being developed, at this time, to address this concern.

In may cases, building services are being managed by third party Building Management companies. Specialist communications companies could enhance the Building Management company by forming a consortium to offer not only the existing building services but also telecommunications as a utility. This approach would ensure continued co-operation and continuity with the building owner but, at the same time, give the assurance that this highly specialised field is being appropriately administered. There are, of course, individual companies who can manage parts of the concept. It is essential, though, that if both the tenant and the building owner are to benefit from an integrated, centrally provided communications strategy, its management and development must be in concert with other building services.

It is envisaged that a management team would either be on-site or the service would be monitored remotely. In either case, resilience would be built into the network to ensure that the system would not collapse if an individual component failed.

This management team would undertake all problem monitoring and resolution, including co-ordination of engineers. Appropriate equipment maintenance, enhancement and replacement would also be the management team's responsibility. In addition, to these traditionally accepted activities, the management team can provide an in-house consultancy service to tenants for the provision and development of their individual requirements.

## 7. CLOSING COMMENTS

The development of standards and products, within the telecommunications industry, is enabling the centralised provision of an integrated building communications system, to be taken seriously.

By presenting telecommmunications as a building utility, managed and enhanced with other building services, both the tenant and the building owner will enjoy tangible and intangible benefits.

By employing the skills of a consortium of specialist companies the integrity of the concept will be assured.

# Electrotechnology for high-tech buildings

ANDREW N JACKSON
B.Tech(Hons), C.Eng., MIMechE, MCIBSE
SENIOR ENGINEER
ELECTRICITY COUNCIL
GREAT BRITAIN

This paper discusses the energy requirements of modern office buildings against the background of the increased use of electronic office equipment, deeper plan buildings and better thermal characteristics.

Cost effective methods for achieving heat recovery are described which in the author's view, are suitable for the majority of speculative and purpose-designed high-tech office buildings.

Andrew Jackson joined the Electricity Council in 1979 where he has been involved with extensive research into the development of electrical methods of heating and airconditioning of modern buildings. He currently conducts negotiations with leading property developers on behalf of the Electricity Supply Industry.

He is Chairman of the London and South East Region of the Chartered Institution of Building Services Engineers.

Presented at HIGH-TECH BUILDINGS 87: Online Publications, Pinner, UK, 1987

The term 'high-tech buildings' means many things to many people.
Within the property industry it is the by-word for the
multi-functional building and the range of uses include R & D
and 'soft' production and often extends to the extremes of
electronic office and simple warehouse space.

Heating and airconditioning systems have to reflect this broad
spectrum of possible use and such systems must be totally
flexible in design and operation.  One factor, however is certain;
the increasing use of electronic equipment throughout offices,
coupled with the tendency to provide deeper plan buildings to
maximise on floor space and the improvement in the  thermal
characteristics of buildings generally, ensure that internal heat
gains will rise.  The emerging pattern of energy supply to such
premises is changing since the level of internal heat generation
is often sufficient to meet a significant proportion of heating
requirements during the occupied period.  Preheating the building
can demand around 50% of the total heating energy supplied.

## Building Heat Gains and Losses

When considering the design of building services systems for
offices which are likely to be equipped with electronic machines
for data processing and communications, it is no longer appropriate simply to estimate the 'design' heat loss and heat gain at
specific ambient temperatures.  An anlysis of the energy
requirement should be carried out to evaluate the heating and
cooling needs throughout the year and, particularly, the
preheating load.

Considering, as an example, the winter-time operation of a building
having a proportion of office area with an occupation density of
one person per 8 $m^2$.  Assuming that a desk-top PC is provided at
each workstation and that such a machine has a continuous heat
dissipation of 360 W, then the heat gain to the space from these
sources alone will be approximately 56 $W/m^2$.  This will be in
addition to heat gains from lighting and peripheral equipment
such as printers which could be 15 – 20 $W/m^2$ depending on
whether high efficiency light sources are used.

The fabric heat loss of the building (designed to the current Building Regulations) will be approximately 30 W/m$^2$ and with the publication of the new Regulations later this year, this may well fall to around 15 - 20 W/m$^2$. This presents an oversimplified picture, of course, because internal heat gain does not always occur uniformly throughout the building whilst the fabric heat loss always occurs at the perimeter. In addition energy is required to preheat incoming fresh air for ventilation purposes and, in some instances, reheat is needed to ensure that the conditioned air is delivered at the correct temperature.

Systems are therefore needed which can preheat buildings efficiently and which can collect and remove unwanted heat during the occupied period and redistribute as required to other parts of the building.

Such systems are either modular or based entirely upon central station plant.

Modular Systems - Unitary Heat Pumps

Based upon a 2 pipe heat distribution circuit serving the whole building, this system utilises mini-heat pumps within each zone to supply or reject heat from or into the water circuit (see figure 1). Each heat pump operates completely independently from each other or they can be grouped and controlled together for larger zones. When overheating conditions are reached within the space the heat pumps will operate as water-cooled aircondition-ing units and reject heat into the 2 pipe circuit. They will operate in the reverse cycle when heating is required using the water circuit as heat sink. Heat is thus transferred around the building; excess heat being removed by a cooling tower or air blast cooler and additional heat added when necessary by a boiler or via electric flow boilers or air/water heat pumps.

Air/water heat pumps can of course provide both functions of heat supply and heat rejection. Since a large part of the heating energy requirements are needed to preheat the building, the external source heat pumps can take advantage of day/night electricity tariffs as well as an average coefficient of performance of approximately 2.5. For a typical office floor, each mini-heat pump will be sized for approximately 20 - 25 m$^2$ of floor area according to the loads for cooling in the space. The two pipe distribution circuit will be nominally 27°C but can fluctuate between 20°C and 30°C. Systems which incorporate blast coolers instead of cooling towers can tolerate water temperatures upto 40°C.

The system is completely flexible. The internal heat pumps can be located either in the ceiling void, floor void or wall mounted at the perimeter of the building. Units can be added, removed or relocated easily to accommodate changing needs of occupiers. In fact, the new headquarters building of a well known company which uses this system has installed each heat pump with flexible connections! This serves to illustrate how often internal spaces may be rearranged by the end user.

A typical installation of a modular heat pump system within a high-tech or multi-functional building of, say, 2 storeys would employ a two-pipe distribution circuit within the ground floor ceiling void. This circuit would not normally need to be insulated because of the relatively small uplift in water temperature over room temperature. Since the normal procedure would be to fit out the upper storey as offices, modular heat pumps would be provided at the perimeter and served from the lower storey ceiling void below. The lower storey itself would be provided with capped branch connections so that the eventual tenant may arrange the space to suit his own requirements. The ceiling void in many instances being used for the heat pumps serving the ground floor. This is clearly a very efficient way of providing an HVAC system which is flexible both in terms of installation and operation. Simultaneous heating and cooling, with heat recovery, is provided throughout and, as a result, virtually infinite zoning is possible. Such systems can be installed for around £100 per $m^2$ floor area.

One example of the use of modular heat pumps in an office building is provided by the Vauxhall Cross building in London. The net floor area is 5,500 $m^2$. External source air/water heat pumps are also used to provide additional heating and hence the building is all-electric. The 5-storey building employs 240 wall mounted units and was designed to be controlled by a building management system. The monitored total annual energy consumption for the building is 155 kWh/$m^2$ pa. The energy costs for the HVAC system is estimated at £5.50/$m^2$ pa.

Central Station Systems

Space does not permit me to evaluate here all the options available for central station equipment which provide a flexible approach to HVAC and heat recovery. There have been some important developments, however, in recent years which deserve mention because, I believe, they could revolutionise the approach to heating and airconditioning in modern offices.

In the 1970s heat recovery was usually achieved by large water cooled chillers equipped with double-bundle condensers. The cost of such equipment confined their use to large buildings and owner-occupiers. When the end user of the project could be identified from inception, it was possible to evaluate the level of heat regeneration by a knowledge of the company's own

office equipment and,in theory at least, to enable an assessment
of the cost-in-use benefit of heat recovery airconditioning.
Since the majority of office building at the time, as today, was
promoted by developers for speculative purposes, rather than
owner-occupiers,there was only limited scope for the use of heat
recovery airconditioning.
stage.

Recently heat recovery equipment has become simpler, compact and
to a certain extent, packaged.  In addition the power requirements
of particular office users have become more predictable. The trend
towards air-cooled airconditioning equipment for larger buildings
has encouraged the development of heat pumps capable of providing
300 kW of heat from a single unit.  Heat pumps have developed
in  other ways too.  By incorporating an additional water cooled
condenser these machines can either reclaim heat from the
ambient air, or alternatively, heat may be reclaimed from the
chilled water circuit.  Such equipment may operate in any of
the following modes;

1.      Water/Water heat pump (heat recovery chiller).

2.      Air/Water heat pump (providing heat).

3.      Air/Water chiller (providing chilled water).

4.      Chiller with heat recovery.

5.      Heat pump with chilled water 'recovery'.

All this can be provided from one item of plant which is no  larger
than a normal air cooled chiller.  A further advantage of this
type of central station heat recovery heat pump  is the fact
that it does not require any plant room space.  It needs free
access to ambient air and therefore can be roof  mounted or
situated at ground level adjacent to the building which it serves.
Figures 2,3 and 4 show  typical installations of a heat recovery
heat pump with both fan coil and variable air volume systems.

## Exhaust Air Heat Pumps

Exhaust air heat pumps combine the principle of a cross-flow heat exchanger with a heat pump to produce an effective means of recovering waste heat from exhaust air which would otherwise be lost from the building.

These devices are usefully employed for single zone areas having a medium to high fresh air requirement. Offices, laboratory and production areas are common applications as well as department stores and shopping malls. A typical packaged system is shown in Figure 5. Supply air to, and exhaust air from, the building are passed through a plate recuperator where approximately 60-70% heat transfer efficiency may be obtained.

The heat transfer may be improved substantially by the addition of a heat pump within the 'package'. By positioning the evaporator and condenser of the heat pump in the air ducts after the heat exchanger, a seasonal coefficient of performance (COP) of between 5 and 6 should be obtained. In summer-time, cooling may be obtained by reverse-cycling the heat pump.

A particular advantage of the exhaust air heat pump is the ability to provide the ventilation heat load and to go some way towards meeting the fabric heat load of the building. In most installations, supplementary heat will be required for the system to provide the full 'design' heating duty.

Figure 7 shows the performance characteristics of a typical exhaust air heat pump. The upper diagram also shows a weather dependent curve and gives the heating demand throughout the year for a zone having a heat loss of 30 kW. The area under the curve represents the energy consumption and it can be seen that the area which falls outside the limit of operation of the exhaust air heat pump represents the amount of additional heat required. This amount is in fact only a small proportion of the total heating energy required throughout the year and it may well prove uneconomic, on the basis of total cost-in-use, to install conventional boiler plant to meet this duty. A simple, direct-acting electric heat battery would, in many circumstances, be more cost-effective. However an analysis should be carried out at the design stage to determine the cost-in-use for each alternative supplementary heating source.

The lower diagram in figure 7 explains the sequence of operation from mid-winter through the season to mid-summer.

## Summary

For high-tech office buildings, heat recovery airconditioning
should be considered at the earliest design stage.  This maxim
embraces buildings for owner-occupiers as well as speculative
developments.  It is due to the high level of internal heat gains
caused by:

1    The widespread, and increasing, use of electronic
     equipment for everyday office tasks.

2    The deep plan design commonly employed for office
     buildings.

3    A significant, and continuing, improvement in the
     thermal characteristics of new buildings.

Heat recovery airconditioning has evolved from the large, water-
cooled chilling machines of the '70s to smaller, packaged air-
cooled equipment suitable for roof mounting, and capable of
providing heating, cooling and heat recovery simultaneously.  Such
equipment may be installed as part of virtually any type of
airconditioning system; variable air volume, fan-coil or induction.

Modular, internal heat pumps provide an alternative method of
heat collection and distribution around the building.  Because of
their inherent flexibility they are particularly suited to the
multi-functional office development and their reduced central plant
requirement often means they are commonly employed in refurbished
buildings.

Airconditioning and ventilation systems all discharge warm exhaust
air from buildings to a greater or lesser degree.  All such systems
require fresh air which must be preheated and/or reheated before
it reaches the conditioned space.  Exhaust air heat pumps can
effectively reclaim this heat and, consequently, provide the fresh
air heating load. In many instances a proportion of the fabric heat
load may be provided, and cooling can be achieved by reversing the
cycle of operation in summer.

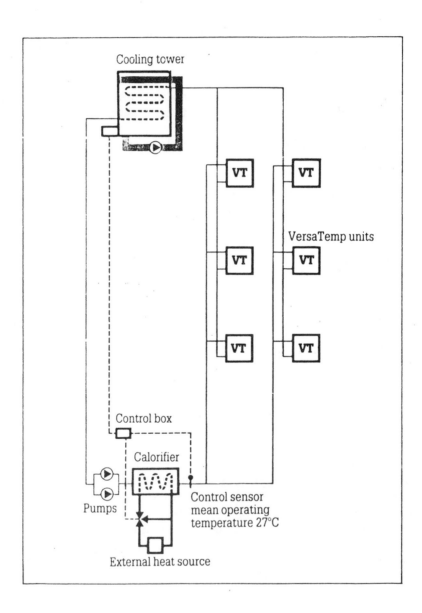

Cooling tower

VT   VT

VersaTemp units

VT   VT

VT   VT

Control box

Calorifier

Control sensor
mean operating
temperature 27°C

Pumps

External heat source

Schematic of Unitary Heat Pump System – Figure 1
(Courtesy of Temperature Ltd)

# FOUR PIPE FAN COIL SYSTEM

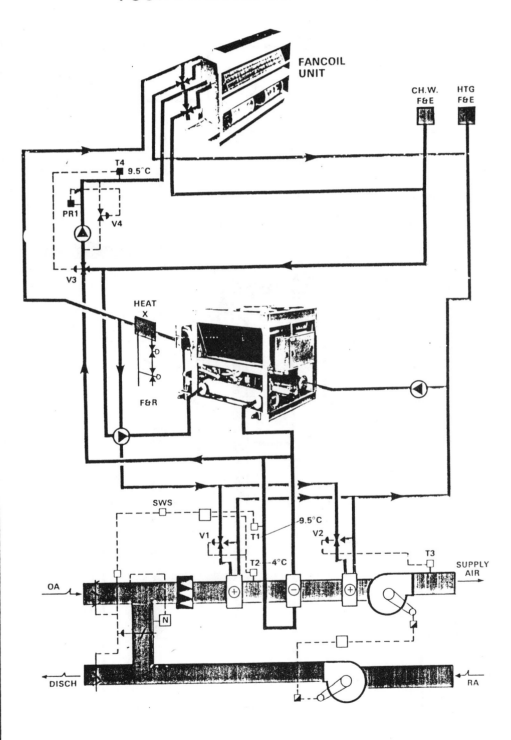

(Courtesy of York International Ltd) – Figure 2

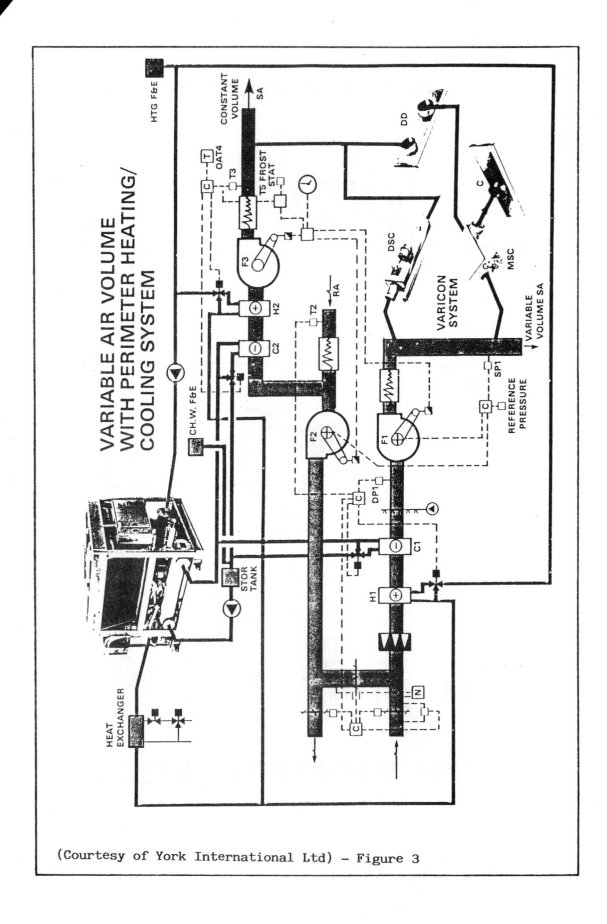

## VARIABLE AIR VOLUME WITH PERIMETER HEATING/COOLING SYSTEM

(Courtesy of York International Ltd) - Figure 3

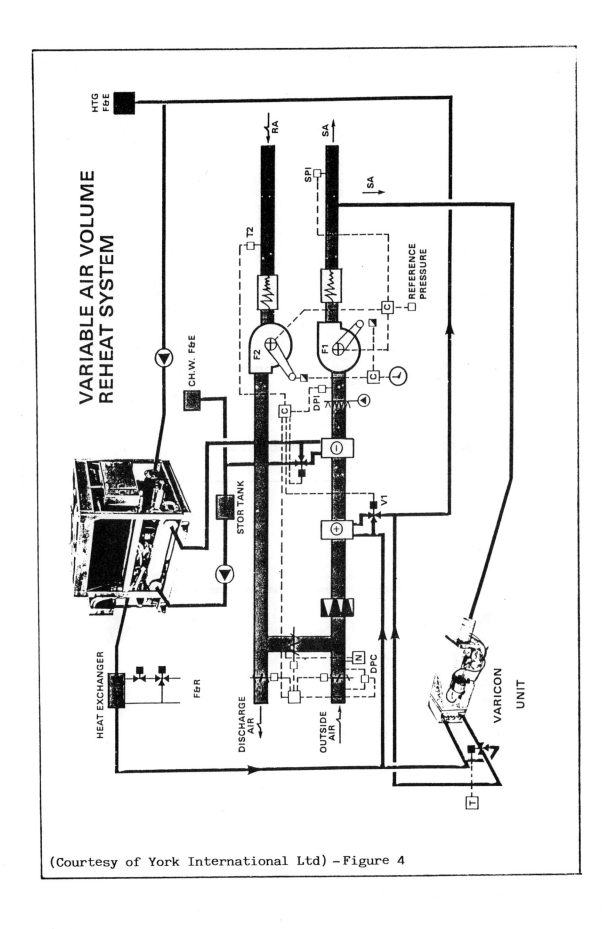

VARIABLE AIR VOLUME REHEAT SYSTEM

(Courtesy of York International Ltd) – Figure 4

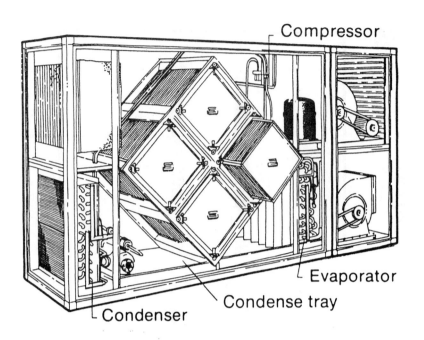

Arrangement of Exhaust Air Heat Pump – Figure 5

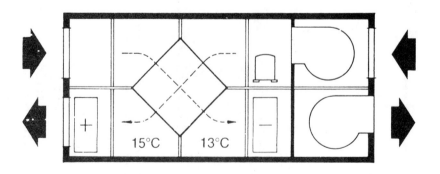

Principle of Operation – Exhaust Air Heat Pump – Figure 6
(Courtesy of Dantherm Ltd)

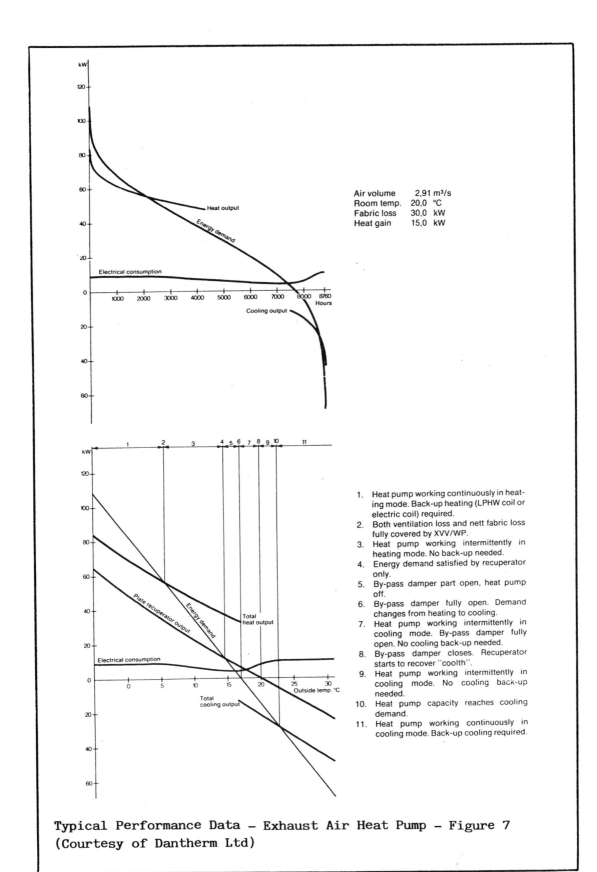

**Typical Performance Data – Exhaust Air Heat Pump – Figure 7 (Courtesy of Dantherm Ltd)**

# Fibre lights the high-tech building

*Berwyn Roberts*
*Marketing Director*
*Pilkington Communication Systems Limited*
*U.K.*

*Voice video and data communications requirements in modern businesses are increasing daily, but current buildings are not designed to cope. The Orbit Report reinforces this view in the following elegant statement 'at the dawn of information technology we have offices which are totally unprepared for the challenge'. Many ducts are already full and this is restricting the ability of companies to put more technology at the desk. Relocation to new premises is an extremely expensive and often unnecessary solution to the problem. Not only does fibre optics offer better utilisation of service ducts, but a whole range of opportunities to make businesses more secure, as well as efficient.*

*Berwyn Roberts is a Marketing Manager with more than 10 years experience in data processing, real time computing, data communications management consultancy and technical marketing. His current responsibilities include the USA marketplace, as well as Europe, and he has a close involvement with Pilkington Security Equipment Limited.*

Presented at HIGH-TECH BUILDINGS 87: Online Publications, Pinner, UK, 1987

## I.   *TRENDS IN INFORMATION TRANSFER*

*Over the last few years there has been an explosion in the number of personal computers and computer terminals in office environments.*

*Computer terminals need to be linked into their host computer requiring a large number of bulky cables probably housed in under-floor ducts. Until recently most personal computers were standalone devices which just did local word processing or spreadsheet tasks. The development of local area networks and associated multi-user software has led to the evolution of integrated networks providing inter-connectivity and the facility to share resources e.g. central file servers and gateways. The servers provide central information banks and printing capability which can be shared between all the users, whilst gateways provide access to other information systems e.g. other local area networks, distant computers via PTT networks, public databases such as Prestel.*

*Complementing the growth in the number of microcomputers and terminals at desks, has been a large growth in the amount of data transmitted. This has led to higher and higher data rates. Current local area networks run at between 4 and 10 megabits per second, whereas the next generation of LANS will have 100 megabit plus capabilities.*

*As well as a growth in the transmission of data there has been a growth in voice and video communications, all of which have to be supported by cabling systems.*

*The increase in computer terminals, printers etc., has also greatly increased the need for power cables. The net result of more data cables, voice links and power cables than the architect ever dreamed possible is that the ducting and risers in many buildings are full to capacity.*

## II.   *TRADITIONAL CABLES*

*Data in traditional cables is carried on internal copper wires as a series of electrical pulses which radiate electric and magnetic fields. However, the cables themselves are also affected by any Electro Magnetic Interference (EMI) in such a way that the data carried may be unreadable when received. The faster the data rates being carried the greater the interference effect. In copper based systems the signal power decreases rapidly with distance as the frequency increases, this is not a problem in fibre optic systems.*

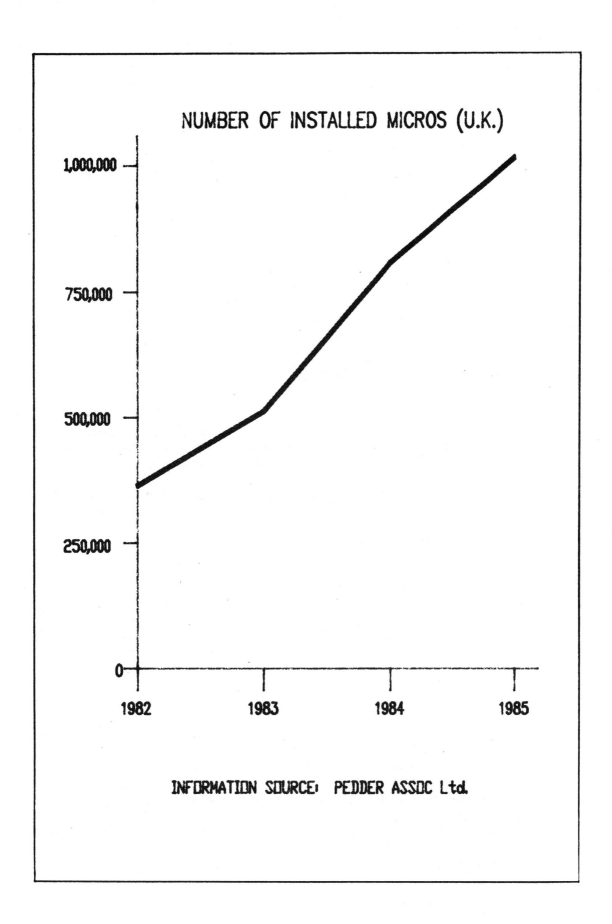

NUMBER OF INSTALLED MICROS (U.K.)

INFORMATION SOURCE: PEDDER ASSOC Ltd.

The constraints that the above place on cabling in a building include:-

a) It is not possible to run data cables alongside power cables.

b) In order to pack data cables close together you have to incorporate some electro magnetic shielding which makes the resulting cable:-

  - heavier
  - bulkier
  - more expensive

c) Data cables should not be routed close to electrical machinery such as lift motors, photocopiers, drinks machines and fluorescent lights.

d) When this electrical machinery is relocated it can introduce problems into existing data transmission paths.

e) If data rates in existing cable runs are increased (typically when changing the type of terminal) data corruption can suddenly become a problem.

f) For high frequency transmissions the transmission distance is limited without use of expensive repeaters.

III. PROPERTIES OF OPTICAL FIBRE

Immunity

Messages are passed along optical fibres as pulses of light and are not affected by electromagnetic radiation. Thus fibre optic cables can be run alongside power cables. Some companies have used high tension transmission lines to support their optical cables.

Capacity

Optical fibre has tremendous data carrying capacity and in Telecoms applications, special singlemode fibres driven by lasers have achieved 1,000 megabits per sec. Inside buildings the shorter transmission distances allow the use of low cost high reliability light emitting diodes (instead of lasers) and multimode fibre while still offering transmission speeds of several hundred megabits over several kilometers. Multimode fibre has the advantage of allowing easier and cheaper terminations to be made.

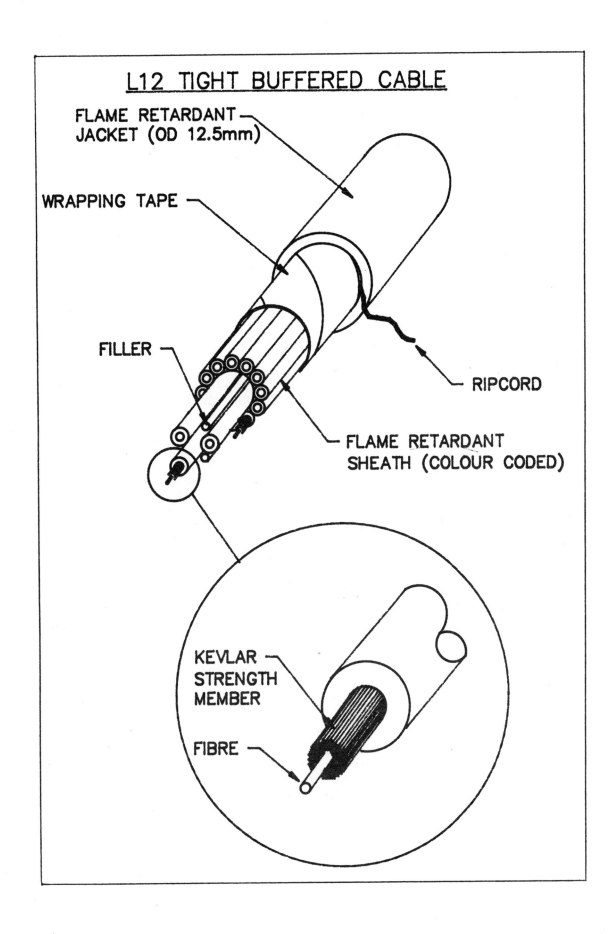

# L12 TIGHT BUFFERED CABLE

FLAME RETARDANT JACKET (OD 12.5mm)

WRAPPING TAPE

FILLER

RIPCORD

FLAME RETARDANT SHEATH (COLOUR CODED)

KEVLAR STRENGTH MEMBER

FIBRE

## Distance

Optical fibre is able to carry signals further without deterioration than copper wire. With 200 micron fibre, transmission distances of several kilometres are common. This is more than adequate for most buildings, and by moving to thinner fibre, tens of kilometer distances become possible.

## Emissions

Security is one of the biggest worries among computer users. Because optical fibre does not emit electromagnetic radiation, it is not possible to eavesdrop on the information being carried. This area has become much more important of late.

## Tapping

It is very difficult to tap into optical fibre. A highly skilled technician can tap into optical fibre but the loss of light can easily be detected.

## Error Rates

Optical fibre is extremely reliable and accurate. The bit error rates associated with fibre optic cables are better than one bit in 1000 million. Reliability of this order enables simpler error checking routines to be used.

## Size and Weight

It must be stressed that it is difficult to make exact comparisons since there are thousands of different types of cable of both types. However, two typical cables are shown below:-

|                      | Outside Diameter(mm) | Weight(Kg/Km) |
|----------------------|----------------------|---------------|
| (1 wire) COPPER      | 6.2                  | 57            |
| (2 fibre) FIBRE OPTIC | 4.8                 | 18            |

If you bear in mind that the fibre optic cable has two fibres and has a much higher data carrying capacity, then in certain situations the single F.O. cable can replace many equivalent copper based cables.

*If we now move into multicore cables the ability to put a
bundle of thin fibres together without EMI shielding to
separate them leads to a dramatic improvement in the F.O.
cable size and weight advantage.*

|  | Outside Diameter(mm) | Weight kg/km |
|---|---|---|
| 10 Way Fibre Optic | 11 | 130 |
| 10 way Coax (3270 type) | 26 | 456 |

### Shorting

*Optical cables have no grounding or shorting problems.  If a
fibre cable is broken, there is no chance of electrical
shock, no sparks, no fire hazard.*

### Conductivity

*Optical fibres do not conduct electricity and as a result
are quite often used as conductor path breaks eliminating
earth loops and providing some protection in case of
lightning strikes.*

### Strength

*When protected in nylon buffer tubes in conjunction with
strength members e.g. Kevlar, optical cables can have very
high tensile strengths and high crush resistance.*

## IV.   COST COMPARISONS

*The costing of fibre optic systems versus copper based
cables is extremely complex since there are so many factors
to consider, including:-*

- *system lifespan*
- *distance*
- *transmission speed*
- *installation costs*

## - *System Lifespan*

*If the system is to last several years then possible expansion in terms of more cable or faster data rates, must be evaluated. If faster data rates will be required it may be necessary at some later stage to rip out the existing copper cable and replace it with fibre optic cable with the very expensive labour costs, in addition to the cable costs. If more cable is going to be required is there sufficient space in the ducts for expansion?*

## - *Distance*

*Over very short distances copper based systems always win on a pure cost basis, since there is no need for line drivers Existing equipment with standard RS232 or RS422 parts have built in line driving electronics; so that the electronics to convert to opticals signals and back again tip the scales in favour of the copper based system. As distances get longer the copper system also requires line driving electronics. At even longer distances, the copper based systems require repeaters, which is not the case with fibre.*

We have already seen how, due to EMI problems, copper cables will often have to follow longer paths than fibre optic cables. Thus in many installations, if the cable lengths are carefully evaluated, a much shorter length of fibre optic cable is required than an equivalent copper cable.

## - *Transmission Speed*

*For low transmission speeds, copper based systems are normally quite adequate, however as transmission speeds increase the problems of signal attenuation (loss) and susceptibility to EMI rapidly increase.*

## - *Installation Costs*

*Quite often the installation costs greatly exceed the cost of the equipment installed. In cases where the ducts become more crowded the labour costs involved will increase - another example of hidden costs.*

## V.  MULTIPLEXING

So far we have looked at the direct attributes of fibre optics and seen that distance, transmission speeds, EMI resistance and security favour fibre optics over copper based solutions.

In many situations it is possible to have the best of both worlds by using multiplexers. Multiplexers (or muxs for short) combine many slow channels of data and send them to another mux over a high speed channel where they are re-assembled into the constituent slow channels.

In multi-storey office blocks, multiplexers are a cost effective way of linking the computer usually located in the basement with terminals on the upper storeys.

## VI.  OPPORTUNITIES RELATED TO FIBRE OPTIC CABLES

### Ducts

Easiest to visualise is the opportunity to use existing cabling ducts to cope with future needs of a continuously expanding population of computer terminals.

The other side of the coin is that new buildings need not be designed with such large ducts and deep false floors. In a high rise office block more floors may be accommodated in the same height.

### Networks

At this moment most fibre optic networks do not meet the complete needs of large buildings since they do not

-   have sufficient bandwidth
-   enable easy access at any point

However a new generation of very high speed fibre optic networks are beginning to emerge which are backed by international standards.

The X3T9.5 committee of The American National Standards Institute currently specify a Fibre Distributed Data Interface (FDDI) which comprises a token passing ring operating at 100 Mbits/sec. The ring will support up to 1000 nodes, with a maximum distance of 2Km between nodes and up to 200Km of total circumference. The specification allows various options to suit different companies planned products, thus making the end result very flexible.

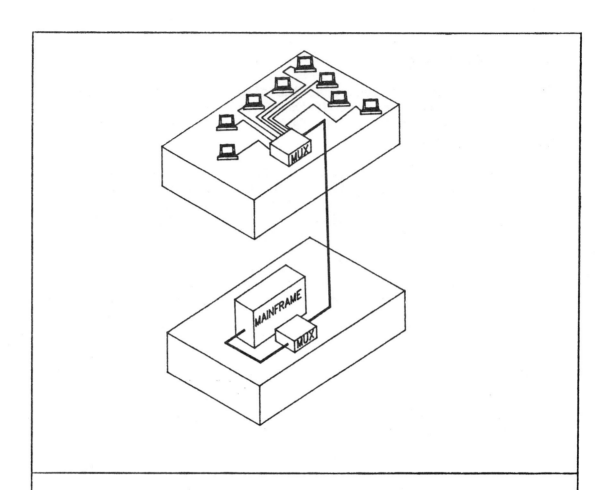

# TIME DIVISION MULTIPLEXING

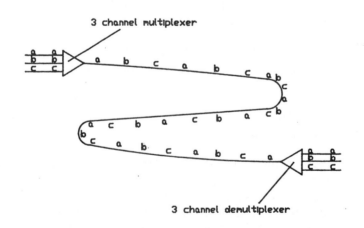

3 channel multiplexer

3 channel demultiplexer

A more sophisticated version of the above called FDDI/II is currently being specified which will allow a whole host of different information forms, including voice, to share a common backbone network, linking a variety of low speed LANS (FDDI as backbone network).

## Data Security

As we have already seen, you cannot eavesdrop into fibre optic cables and tapping is very difficult. One of the current range of available products continually measures the amount of light being transmitted along the optical fibre and if cable intrusion takes place, the data flow is immediately halted and alarms are sounded. This allows data to move between secure areas in a building (e.g. between the Managing Director's office and the PABX or computer) via non-secure areas.

An interesting use of this idea is to put all the processing work of personal computers into a secure environmentally controlled area e.g. the computer room. Apart from the security improvement aspects there are many other spin-offs:

- a shared spare could be kept readily available for emergencies.

- in case of a disk crash, processor failure etc., the problem could be solved without a technician wandering around the dealing room floor etc.

- if there was a software problem the user could ring the computer room, who could "plug" into the processor and solve the problem locally.

- a shared tape streamer could be used to provide a back-up service which would be done regularly by trained personnel.

## Physical Security

The recent Orbit Study carried out by experts from DEGW, EOSYS, and Building Use Studies Ltd., found that security would be an increasing cause of concern.

The Security Industry is plagued with equipment which has high False Alarm Rates (F.A.R.) and also fails to detect intruders. A security system should achieve a high Probability of Detection (P.O.D.) and a low F.A.R.

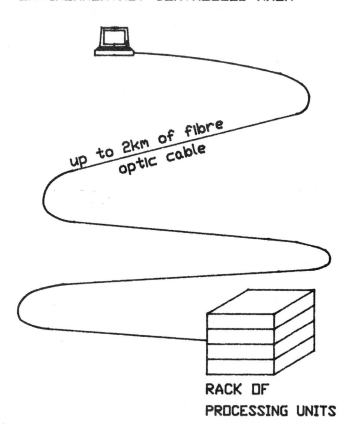

REMOTE SITING OF MICROCOMPUTER
PROCESSING UNIT IN A SECURE
ENVIRONMENTALY CONTROLLED AREA

up to 2km of fibre
optic cable

RACK OF
PROCESSING UNITS

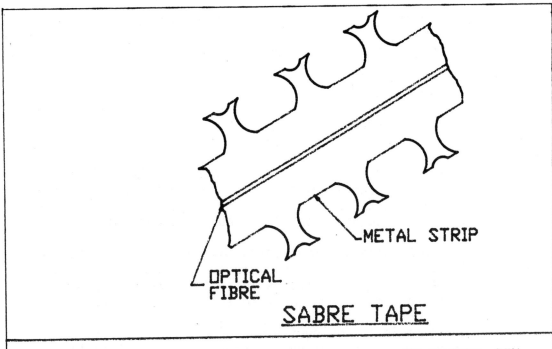

METAL STRIP

OPTICAL FIBRE

## SABRE TAPE

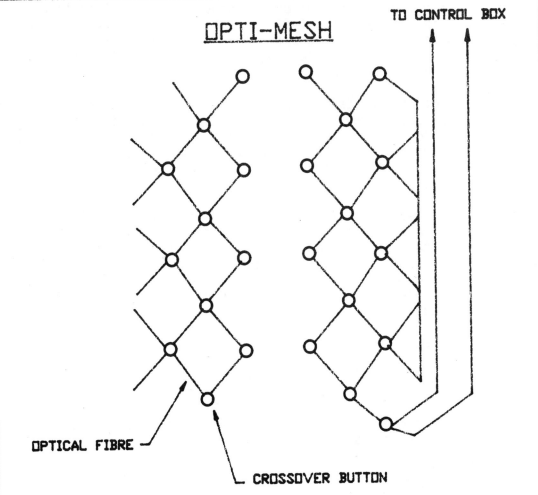

## OPTI-MESH

TO CONTROL BOX

OPTICAL FIBRE

CROSSOVER BUTTON

*Fibre optics are not influenced by conditions which set other sensor systems into an alarm condition*

- *lightning*
- *radios*
- *sun, snow, fog, rain, wind*
- *vibrations*
- *insects and birds*

*Fibre optics can be configured into a variety of safety and security products which enable architects, surveyors and security installers to configure a security system to suit their particular threat type, building and budget.*

*The sophisticated electronics involving clever tricks (e.g. frequent self calibration) are able to make use of the property of optical fibres where the amount of light reaching the end changes when the fibre is bent.*

*One example is the equivalent of a barbed wire fence that cannot be climbed or cut without detection (Sabretape). In this case an optical fibre is bonded to a serrated steel strip and linked at both ends to an alarm system. This form of protection can be mounted on fences, walls, gates or the sides of buildings.*

*Another form is the fibre optic mesh where an optical fibre is clad in Kevlar reinforced sleeving in net form and deployed around walls or vaults, possibly behind plaster or brickwork. This configuration is for long term application and illustrates the variety of fibre optic sensor options available.*

*One recent novel application of this property of optical fibre was in a museum with a largely glass roof. The installation of conventional intrusion detectors were troubled by a variety of problems e.g. birds, warm air rising etc. The solution has been to tape optical fibre to the glass roof panels thus detecting any pressure or breakage.*

## Video

*Video transmission requires a high bandwidth. In cases where distances in excess of several hundred meters are involved, the quality possible with copper based systems rapidly deteriorates. Very expensive and bulky coax cables have to be used.*

## Dealing Rooms

Banks depend on market information from services such as
Reuters, Topic and Telerate. The usual arrangement is for
the normally analogue video signals to be sent via a video
switch to one of the VDU's on the dealers desk. The
connection between the dealer desk and the switch can easily
be in excess of 100 metres in length. This requires very
bulky coax cable and vertical visers can soon become full,
hence banks are pioneers in the use of fibre optic cables
e.g. Shearson Lehman Bros, New York have over 2000 dealer
desks connected using approx. 4000 kms of optical fibre.

## Surveillance

Even though the bandwidth required for picture based
surveillance video is much less than for the text based
banking market, the distances can quite often be much
longer. Current technology allows good quality surveillance
video to be transmitted at a low cost over distances of 15km
using fibre optic cable.

## VII.   CONCLUSIONS

Fibre optics has been around for over ten years, however it
is only now gaining general acceptance in the office
environment as a vastly superior transmission medium.

The advent of Open Systems Interconnection (OSI) and new
very high speed fibre optic networks (e.g. FDDI) will allow
a common communications system through the high-tech
building. This negates the problems of full ducts and
overloaded floors.

Other papers in this conference have emphasised the need for
communications facilities to be a centrally provided utility
for which the tenant pays a premium. The cable
infra-structure will have to support a wide range of
interface products (PABX, telex, facsimile, data
communications, video, telemetry etc).

This paper has shown that these requirements will allow
fibre optics to play a major role in high-tech buildings,
both in terms of improving the connectivity of the services
and also offering increased physical and data security. How
soon this happens will of course depend on how fast the
message reaches the majority of decision makers - lets hope
that the UK can be in the forefront.

# Cost effective lighting management

N. Declan Ryan
Director
Illuminated Management Associates
UK

The introduction of a Telephone Interface Unit (**TIU**) by Illuminated Management Associates will allow the occupants of a commercial office to turn **on,** or **off,** their local light fittings through the internal telephone network. As well as providing for total flexibility in the light switching arrangements, the system offers the scope for highly effective lighting control which would lead to dramatic savings in lighting running costs.

A graduate of University College Dublin, Declan has in-depth experience in all aspects of the controls business.

He was responsible for planning the launch of several innovative lighting control products for a subsidary of a major lighting company. He undertook several intensive market research programmes into the lighting control industry before founding Illuminated Management.

At Illuminated Management, Declan was responsible for the **TIU** development Programme. He now directs our Marketing and Sales operations.

Presented at HIGH-TECH BUILDINGS 87: Online Publications, Pinner, UK, 1987

## LIGHTING CONTROL:  A KEY TO EFFECTIVE BUILDING MANAGEMENT

To the vast majority of the occupants of a commercial office, lighting is 'out of sight and out of mind'.  They expect it to be **on** when they enter an area but assume that somebody else will turn it **off.**

The general tendency is, therefore, for the first occupant to turn all the lighting in a given area **on** and for the lighting to be left **on** until the end of normal occupancy.

This tendency to leave the lighting **on** for long periods is compounded by the fact that the lighting in most large commercial offices is generally brought **on** by the Cleaners first thing in the morning.  It then remains **on** until switched **off** by Security last thing at night.

This can lead to typical lighting running hours in excess of 4,500 per year.  If this is compared to the standard occupancy of just under 2,000 hours by the typical occupant, then it can be seen that the excessive lighting running hours lead to the inefficient and wasteful use of energy.

A series of studies by the Building Research Establishment[1] has shown that this pattern of lighting usage can be dramatically altered, with consequential savings in energy consumption, by the introduction of lighting control systems.

Lighting control systems are particularly effective if;

  - they pay particular attention to occupant action.  That is, if a particular occupant is given local control over the local lighting environment.

  - the operation of such control systems take account of local conditions through, for example, turning the lighting **off** at regular intervals in areas with a high level of natural daylight.

This combination of a high degree of local control over the lighting environment, with account being taken of environmental factors, forms the basis of the 'active daylighting' approach to lighting control.

This approach has been highly effective in reducing lighting running costs with minimal impact on the working environment.  In addition, the reduced lighting load can lead to major savings in the cost of chilling the building and in the operation of central plant.

## IF EFFECTIVE - WHY NOT WIDELY USED ?

Despite the fact that this approach to lighting control has been shown to save 40% (and more) of lighting running costs in commercial offices[2], the incorporation of such systems into New Developments, or major refurbishments, has been relatively low.

This reluctance to incorporate lighting control equipment has been ascribed to three inter-related factors;

- firstly, the designer of the Building Services is unlikely to have a detailed knowledge of the eventual Tenant's layout or occupancy requirements until very late in the contract (if at all). There is, therefore, a natural reluctance to undertake the detailed consideration of local environmental factors.

- secondly, the Developer is unlikely to gain directly from the provision of such systems and tends to treat expenditure on increased local/flexible control of lighting as a luxury item. Such items are often the first to be cut when costs come under pressure.

- thirdly, existing lighting control systems are generally of limited flexibility and can be difficult to adapt to meet changing occupant requirements. Such changes normally require alterations to both switch and light fitting wiring.

The recent introduction of a Telephone Interface Unit (**TIU**) by Illuminated Management Associates overcomes these problems and offers the Building Services Manager the prospect of a totally flexible, yet cost-effective solution to the problem of managing change in a commercial office environment.


## THE TELEPHONE INTERFACE SOLUTION

The search for a light switching method that did not rely on 'hard wiring' or expensive external controls, but could be totally integrated with other building services, led us to consider the use of the internal telephone network.

We have therefore developed a unit which will allow the occupant to control the local lighting environment through a switching operation carried out via the internal telephone network. To operate this switching system, it would be simply necessary to dial a single/two digit code to turn **on**, or **off**, light fittings/pre-designated groups of fittings.

Although the code used is general for all extensions in the building (or for all extensions associated with a particular PABX, if the building is multi-tenanted), a given occupant would only control the pre-designated fittings associated with a particular geographical location.

Alterations to these pre-designated groups of fittings can be readily undertaken by means of a simple keyboard operation, or automatically carried out through a computerised up-date system.

Control would be exercised through a **TIU** located near to a digital PABX. This Unit monitors the call logging line from the PABX and responds to a request from an extension for a pre-designated Trunk Route(s). The **TIU** relates its record of the extension requesting this switching operation to a data-base containing the record of Relay Units associated with that extension. It then signals the addressable output(s) controlling the Relay(s) and turns the particular fitting(s) **on, or off.**

The **TIU** is a passive device as far as the PABX (or the Call Logger) is concerned and it cannot, in any way, interfere with the normal operation of the telephone network. The **TIU** has received all necessary approvals etc. from BT Teleprove.


## LIGHTING CONTROL SYSTEM

The **TIU** is a microprocessor based device which can also be programmed to give several levels of control over the lighting.

Our experience, and the work of independent monitoring organisations, indicates that the most effective lighting control systems are those based on the 'manually **on,** but automatically **off,**' philosophy of control. That is, the occupant of a particular workstation should be free to bring **on** the local lighting at any time, but the lighting is turned **off** automatically depending on the time of day and/or local environmental conditions.

We would recommend that the lighting in a particular building be divided into three basic Groups for control purposes. Each of these Groups can be further subdivided into 'patterns' to give a very sophisticated effect with minimal impact on the normal working environment.

These Groups comprise;

i) <u>Health and Safety Lighting</u>: fittings in Lobby areas/Stairwells etc. provide the lighting required for Health and Safety purposes. These fittings are normally outside the scope of a control system, but we would recommend that they are linked to Security via the **TIU**, so that the opportunity can be taken to reduce the levels by e.g., 50% during the 12pm to 6am period.

11) <u>Essential Lighting</u>: Fittings which provide the lighting deemed as being necessary, whether environmental conditions are favourable or not, are designated as Essential. These normally comprise of Core/Corridor lighting fittings on each Floor Level. These fittings would be controlled by momentary contact push-button switches at the entry point to each Floor segment.

These fittings would be turned **on** manually by the first occupants each morning and they would remain **on** for the duration of normal occupancy for that particular segment each day.

The push-button switches would be wired into a Networking Module on the data highway. This would provide full status feedback and allow for automatic **off** control.

iii) <u>Non-Essential Lighting</u>: the remaining fittings would be designated as non-essential. They would normally only be brought **on** through the occupants' use of the telephone system, but they would be turned **off** automatically in response to signals from the timer in the **TIU** (at lunch-time, end of normal occupancy etc.) or through the Building Management System.

The highly sophisticated nature of the **TIU** and the flexibility of telephone switching means that very complicated lighting 'patterns' can be generated. This means that, for example, fittings on the perimeter rows can be turned **off** at given times or under set environmental conditions. Alternatively, set numbers of fittings (eg. 10%) in the building, or in a given Segment, can be turned **off** at any time by the Building Management System.

Please note that the occupants' would be free to override this automatic **off** at any time  through the use of their telephone to bring the fittings back **on** again.

The **TIU** will scan all Essential and Non-Essential fittings at regular intervals during the night to turn **off** any fittings/ groups of fittings brought **on** by Late-Workers or Security.

The use of the **TIU** as a lighting control system would allow the running time of the lighting fittings to be closely matched with normal operational hours.  This would mean a minimum reduction from 4,500 hours per year (a typical example of lighting running hours in City Offices) to well under 3,000 hours per year.  This would lead to major savings in lighting running costs.

The **TIU** can accept signals from any of the major Building Management Systems and its use will allow lighting control to be an integral part of the energy management programme.

## SYSTEM COMPONENTS

A complete telephone switching system would comprise the following basic components;

a) Telephone Interface Unit (**TIU**):  this is a microprocessor driven device which monitors AS11 messages on asynchronous serial lines. Connection to a digital PABX is via approved 1671 Line Drivers to the V24 port used by the Call Logging Unit.  Access to, and interrogation of, the **TIU** is by standard Keyboard/VDU procedures.

Output from the **TIU** is to a 4 core screened cable which carries the data highway to the Networking Modules.  We would strongly recommend that each 'Riser' in a building is provided with its own independent Data Highway.  A standard **TIU** can support up to 4 such highways.

These arrangements ensure that it is not possible for the **TIU** to send information to, or interfere in any way with, the PABX or Call logging Unit.  They have received full BT approval.

b) Networking Module:  this unit will contain all the items necessary to interface between the data highway and individual Relays.  It will contain its own power supply, pcbs etc., and the addressable outputs necessary to control up to 7 Relays.

The Module is connected to the nearest convenient Mains supply by standard 3 core flex.  It is fully opto-isolation protected from the data highway and each Module is individually fused. Connection to the Relays is by 2 core low-voltage cable.

c) Relay Unit:  Each Unit is rated to carry an 8 amp fluorescent load at 240V ac.  The Units can be located in each fitting (or in the circuit to a group of fittings, if more than one fitting is to be controlled by a given relay) and connect to the Networking Module via 2 core low-voltage cable.

d) Push-Button Switches: these are of the momentary contact type. They are used for manual control of the circuits/fittings deemed Essential in any given Segment of a Building. They can be configured to meet the Client's specific requirements.

They can also be used to over-ride the **TIU** so that all lighting in a given Segment can be brought **on** at any time (Security/ emergencies etc.) by means, for example, of a Keyswitch.

The introduction of the Telephone Interface concept by Illuminated Management Associates offers all of those concerned with the design of the modern High-Tech Building the freedom to provide total layout flexibility at minimal cost.

- the **Developer** does not have to pay for facilities that may never be used

- the **Architect** is not constrained by the requirements of inflexible 'hard-wired' control circuits

- the **Consulting Engineer** is offered the opportunity to provide a comprehensive range of control options that can be tailored to meet the requirements of a specific Tenant at a later date

- the **Contractor** has only to deal with a limited amount of wiring

- the **Tenant** is offered total flexibility to meet present and future layout requirements, while, at the same time, has the opportunity to make dramatic savings in the running costs of the building.

The Presentation to the Conference will detail how the principles outlined in this paper have been applied to the installation of a lighting control system, incorporating the **TIU**, in Woolgate House - the U.K. Headquarters of The Chase Manhattan Bank N.A. Details of the savings achieved to-date from the installation will also be provided.

Illuminated Management Associates would like to acknowledge the assistance of the Department of Energy in the development of the Telephone Interface Unit.

References

1 Designing for natural and artificial lighting - BRE Publications AP29  1986

2 Energy Efficiency Demonstration Scheme - A Review  HMSO  1984

# Long life high-tech/a strategy for services

Frank Simmons
Senior Partner
Tilney Simmons and Partners
United Kingdom

Many recently constructed office buildings are already unable to
meet the demands of their occupiers due to the inability of the
engineering services installations to fulfill the needs of the
modern 'high-tech' occupant.

A mix of flexibility, adaptability and highly refined form of
long-life; loose-fit; low-energy can provide the necessary
answers.

The author's practice has for over 20 years, specialised in
designing and adapting engineering services installations for
tenants and owner-occupiers in the banking and financial sector.

Reference is made to specific problems encountered in the past and
how they could have been avoided, if the correct strategies had
been followed.

Frank Simmons was trained and educated
in Mechanical Engineering. His career
has included periods with consultants
and engineering contractors plus
commissioned service in the Royal Air
Force. Latterly, he has been involved
with the whole range of engineering
installations with particular emphasis
on ensuring that owners and occupiers
are provided with the services they
need on a true life cycle/cost
effectiveness basis.

Presented at HIGH-TECH BUILDINGS 87: Online Publications, Pinner, UK, 1987

A large number of office buildings in London are no longer able to fulfill their function properly and economically. The one factor that they all have in common is 'tight fit'. They were designed and constructed in that period when a tenant could be found for almost any office building with the result that the net lettable area had to be maximised regardless of other considerations.  It is true there was no clear indication at the time, that in a mere 20 years, office buildings would be demanding to be serviced to a far higher level.  It should not have taken a genius, to realise that change would one day arrive. The failure which is causing 20 year old buildings to be demolished and replaced, is the failure to allow for change.

Ironically, it was in the 60's that the seeds of 'long life, loose fit, low energy' were sown and the benefits are to be seen in some of the industrial buildings of the day which still survive and operate efficiently in 1987.

The essential quality required to fit today's high tech building for a long and economic life is little more than a refined form of loose fit, low energy.  The important factor is to foresee, as best one can, the kind of changes which can occur.  This has to be approached with care: all the pundits are saying that the heat loads of computers are going down and that eventually, all the data and voice communications will travel down one conductor - or by radio.  One must recall however that the pundits have been saying that computer heat loads would go down for many years and yet we are still building large computer rooms with high electrical loadings. One must surely learn from this that, while technology may well make massive advances, demand for technology is likely to increase even faster.

For the time being, the refined loose fit, low energy high tech building is the only secure answer.

The importance of refinement is obvious; if 'spare' accessible space is to be incorporated into a building it must be done in a carefully controlled way to make sure that when it is wanted it really works and to ensure that the cost penalty is minimised.

This is where good strategic planning of the services is essential.

It is not easy to find a satisfactory definition of good strategic planning which is positive in nature.  It is somewhat simpler to cite instances where events have proved that the strategic planning either was faulty or non-existent.

In commissions where our role has been to fit our client's
activity into a building which he already occupies, we have met
many cases of failure.  So often the failure is of a kind which
makes it almost impossible to reach the right solution: the
disruption and cost involved are simply too great.

As an illustration of this kind of problem, I can recall three
buildings we have been involved with recently where there have
been requirements to alter and enhance the arrangements for
standby power.  All of them had public supplies which had been
installed primarily for lowest first cost and all of them had
standby generators to carry partial load.  The generator supply
had been connected to the building's electrical distribution
system in a way which met the initial requirements, again at
lowest first cost.

In all three buildings, the time came when the occupier needed to
support his operations with a higher coverage of standby power and
in no case was it possible to do this so that the most beneficial
use could be made of the existing generator capacity.  The
electrical networks had been installed in a fragmented way due to
the public supply being taken in the form of multiple low voltage
supplies - which is normally the cheapest way of doing it. Only a
properly integrated network will allow the best use to be made of
a partial standby power installation; moreover only an integrated
network will allow the standby capacity to be increased to cover
the full load without excessive cost and with minimum
vulnerability to failure.

The change in strategic thinking which is necessary, is to
visualise the ultimate level of service which an occupant might
require; and that requires a knowledge of the sort of changes
which tenants make in buildings and the the sort of changes which
they would like to make but don't because of the expense and
disruption.

Applied to the case of the power supply, it means that the
designer must produce a scheme for a fully integrated power supply
system with full standby and, these days, provision for UPS with
its dedicated distribution system. The scheme is first designed to
meet the highest power demand level which is foreseen for the
building. Then the designer superimposes onto the full scheme the
initial requirements which have been identified.

At this point the designer has some crucial decisions to make and
the skill with which he makes them will determine the success of
the process.  He has to incorporate alterations into his original
scheme so that it can be cut back to provide only the initial
requirements whilst retaining the ability to add back the

components required to construct the full power scheme in economic stages and without disruption to operations.

To the designer who is well practiced in this, it is somewhat easier to do than it is to describe: the designer whose involvement is only with the original installation and who then walks away from the job never to know what later changes have been made, is unlikely to find the process so simple.

This same thinking needs to be applied to the air conditioning systems. The buildings being planned today involve greater internal areas than ever before and at the same time a much greater range of internal loads have to be dealt with. It is important to remember that while provision may be made for office equipment heat loads of up to 75 or 100 Watts per square metre, that doesn't mean that those loads will necessarily be installed on a uniform basis through the building. Moreover, the equipment which is installed is not going to be switched on simultaneously nor is it all going to be consuming its rated power supply all the time it is switched on. It is normal to install variable air volume air conditioning systems to deal with the cooling requirements of these internal areas with their high equipment loads and there are a number of points to consider about the situation which results.

Firstly, the ultimate loads which the air conditioning is now called upon to deal with, mean that the duct sizes are considerably larger than have been necessary for internal zones in the past and the alternative of a combination of VAV with some kind of air-water system needs to be considered if only to limit the size of service voids. It must be borne in mind also, that the large open areas now being demanded, free from columns, service cores and other obstructions, will lead to very long duct runs in false ceiling spaces; this will increase the size of the ducts and this is another reason for looking at combination systems.

Secondly, a complicating factor in the design of VAV systems is the manner chosen to maintain the fresh air ventilation rates at a constant level regardless of the variation of total air delivered by the VAV system under changing loads. Not only can this lead to complex control solutions but it is rarely possible to achieve the level of economy which is desirable.

A third more serious problem relates to the need of the VAV terminals to turn down during periods of low load. For a number of reasons it is considered good practice to limit the turn-down range of VAV terminals so that the minimum air supplied is not less than between 40% to 60% of the maximum, depending on the type of air distribution used. With the large equipment loads now

being predicted in internal areas it is quite possible for
equipment loads to represent 80% of the total cooling load
including people and lights. This would mean that the VAV
terminal would have to turn down to say 20% of the maximum when
the equipment is not in use. Where this problem is recognised in
existing installations it is usually solved by installing terminal
re-heat on the VAV units. This is potentially a disastrous
waste of energy although it might be reduced by using reclaimed
heat if it is available. Electric re-heat used for this purpose
would take a lot of justifying.

It is clear that a simple decision at the conceptual stage to air
condition such a building with a VAV system must be questioned
strongly. The proper level of investigation of the requirements
and objectives, the right application of strategic thought would
demonstrate that the alternative of a base VAV system combined
with some form of air-water system, perhaps a combination of two
and four pipe fan coil systems, would give a better initial
response at marginal additional cost and would provide a much
better basis for subsequent enhancement. There is another dilemma
which arises from these much higher equipment loads which are
becoming commonplace today.

It is known that the levels quoted are almost certainly only going
to be experienced in parts of the building; sometimes the extent
may be predicted, at least in the short term, but it may be
impossible to determine with any confidence, where in the building
the heavily loaded areas may be situated. Some developers briefs
are responding to this by accepting the simple view that the only
solution is to equip the whole building to meet the high equipment
gains.

Experience has shown that there is an alternative solution. It
requires a prediction to be made, for the initial occupation, of
what the peak equipment load might be, to what proportion of the
usable space it will apply and what is the level of loading to be
assumed for the remaining area. This gives a readily calculated
average load from which can be derived the initial capacity of the
public power supply and of any standby plant to be installed.

We have developed an approach which allows the system to be
designed with a blend of flexibility and adaptability, so that the
extent to which the system has excess capacity for the initial
load is minimised. The space required for additional plant to
raise the loading to the ultimate level is determined and the
means for connecting the additional capacity into the system, so
as to minimise later shut-downs, are also decided.

The result is a plant installation which is not oversized for its demand and distribution networks which have inherent flexibility to allow a choice to be made of the location and extent of the areas of peak load - within the overall limits of the installed capacity of the building. The network is designed to allow for upgrading the loading of the building with minimum cost and disruption to the occupiers operations.

In this context the term 'flexibility' refers to a system or component part which has been selected so that it can, without significant alteration, meet the demands of a different design condition than that which was originally specified. By 'adaptability' is meant that the system or component has been so designed that it can be readily and economically altered, enhanced or added to with minimum disruption to the normal operations of the building.

As far as the plant is concerned, the process is one of determining the optimum modular arrangement so that the ultimate capacity can be installed in a suitable number of stages. The design of the distribution networks to meet this objective is considerably more complicated and over the years a number of approaches have been developed to meet the required objectives.

One example of this approach, which has stood the test of time, is the main computer centre for BACS, the interbank clearing organisation which also handles the transfer of funds for a vast range of commercial and industrial customers. This centre was built in 1970 with a data processing area of some 2800 sq. m. and was intended to provide for the organisation's needs for many years to come. The initial design level for computer equipment was an average of 330 Watts per sq. m. At the same time it was recognised that load concentrations would be experienced which would considerably exceed the average level. The system was therefore designed so that zones could be increased in capacity up to a level of 660 Watts per sq. m., to the point where the installed plant capacity was equalled. This was system flexibility.

At the same time, space was left so that further air handling plant could be installed to increase the loading of any zone to 1100 Watts per sq. m. - once again up to the limit of the installed cooling plant capacity. Further space was left so that additional primary plant could be installed to increase the overall capacity to an average loading of 660 Watts per sq. m. All of the these changes were capable of being made without any disruption to the Centre's operations. Further enhancement beyond this point was not considered likely but could be carried out at the cost of needing some shut-down time. This came under the heading of adaptability.

The Centre has now been in full continuous operation, for 24 hours a day, seven days a week, for over 15 years and has demonstrated the robustness of the features which were incorporated to allow for change. As the operational requirements for the Centre have increased and changed over the years further plant has been added, the internal arrangement of the room has been changed a number of times, and some plant has had to be renewed due to wear and tear but by and large, the measures included to minimise disruption due to change have proved successful.

The same principles, with the addition of some of the lessons learnt from 15 years of continuous involvement with this Centre have been applied to the design of the new headquarters building under construction at Hemel Hempstead for BP Oil.

This is a new greenfield site development of some 45,000 sq. m. in two buildings. The larger building contains offices and supporting areas on 4 floors each of some 4500 sq. m. net area with basement storage and car parking. This is a country house style building with office departments which are separated from each other by stair and service cores and which are arranged round an atrium which runs through the L-shaped plan of the building. The lower floors are open to the atrium.

The second building houses staff amenity areas on 3 floors.

The complex also includes a computer facility with a total DP space of 2000 sq. m.

Linking the basement of the main building across to the basement of the staff amenity building is the area where heavy plant is installed. Cooling towers are installed on the roof of the main building while the generator and boiler flues terminate on the roof of the amenity building.

The site carries external car parking and a dedicated substation as well as staff recreation facilities.

Air handling plant for the computer centre are in a plant strip alongside the computer room while those for the offices are situated on the main building roof.

The main debate on services policies centred on the distributed power level to be designed for office electronic equipment; the best way of dealing with the planning freedom which the client required to interchange cellular offices and open office areas.

Since this was a combination of office and computer centre, the source of primary power was a very important issue. The air conditioning system design needed to be selected to allow for the internal loads and to provide for the planning flexibility.

Determining the policy for primary power was the subject of exhaustive studies. Since the development combined office and amenity areas which would require the input of heat during at least some winter hours and the computer centre would be a source of waste heat at virtually all hours, there was a strong possibility that either a total energy system with full on-site power generation or, at the very least a partial on-site generation system for either peak-lopping or base load generation using the public supply for topping up, would be a viable solution.

Design studies for a wide variety of solutions ranging from total energy through various mixes of partial energy to the conventional solution of public supply backed up by standby generators were carried out in detail. These looked at all the aspects of cost effectiveness and pay-back on investment. Any financial advantages shown by the on-site generation options were extremely marginal when all factors were taken into account. When the risks of future changes in those factors, such as fuel costs, growth or decline in the availability of waste heat, changes in the operating patterns of the computer centre etc., were considered, it was seen that the risk of the total energy or partial energy solutions becoming non-viable were considerable. There was a real possibility that the client would be left with a major investment in engineering plant which could no longer pay its way and we agreed that the right solution was to adopt the conventional approach.

Another area of intensive study was the determination of the office equipment power levels. Initially we suggested for the conceptual design stage, an average level of 25 Watts per sq. m. This was some time ago now and the proposals were regarded as on the high side. However, BP, who are leaders in the use of distributed computing in an integrated system, set their information technology specialists the task of recommending the power levels which were necessary to enable the building to fulfill its purpose into the 21st century.

The design levels ultimately agreed was an average over all office area of 35 Watts per sq. m. with the ability to serve peaks of up to 75 Watts per sq. m. over 10% of the total area. It was further necessary to be sufficiently flexible to enable relocation of the areas of higher heat gain in the future.

This had to be taken into account in the design of the air conditioning which for reasons which I outlined earlier was a combination of VAV plus fan-coil with an increased capacity secondary distribution network with provision for plugging in additional fan-coil units, either floor standing or ceiling mounted, in areas where they were called for by future growth.

It is also important, when flexibility of load distribution is a feature of the brief, to realise that the way the pipe networks are routed through the building takes on a new dimension. The usual factors which determine where the service spaces can be situated so that they can carry the distribution network to connect all the output points, to occupy space which is least useful for other purposes but is nevertheless adequate and accessible. These are joined by a further consideration. The routing of the service spaces can have a considerable impact on the economy with which flexibility can be incorporated into the design.

The setting of the right servicing strategies for a modern high tech building which will serve its purpose at least to the middle of the 21st century is more than just a series of glib answers tripped lightly off the speaker's tongues at a three day conference. It is a very diverse subject, simply because engineering services cover a very diverse field and they need to be handled in very different ways. The only rules for proceeding which make any sense are:

(1)  Make sure that the objectives for the building now and in the future are fully understood.

(2)  Make full use of experience of the last 30 years - what are the alterations which have been called for and how, where possible, have they been accomplished.

(3)  Don't accept glib answers. Make sure everyone thinks properly about what they are doing.

(4)  Above all, don't be misled into thinking that solutions used by others must necessarily be right for you. There may be superficial similarities but there are likely to be fundamental but subtle differences.

# Today's intelligent building

William S Watson, B.Sc. MBA
General Manager
International Division
BICC Transmitton
UK

The increasing content of data processing, telecommunications, building automation and the related wiring within a building is changing the nature of the design, construction and management of buildings. It is calling more and more for a systems solution from suppliers of systems and products including "one stop shopping" integrated systems design with built-in "future proofing" and a comprehensive building management service. Although developers and suppliers in the USA are responding to this change, Europe is slower to react with its more fragmented building market.

William Watson, after working for a number of years in the cable and construction side of the BICC Group, moved to Transmitton where, for most of the last 8 years, he has been involved in setting up their Building Management System division and, more recently, expending their operations overseas.

Presented at HIGH-TECH BUILDINGS 87: Online Publications, Pinner, UK, 1987

## INTRODUCTION

In theory, the better the design of a building its systems and support services, the greater the efficiency and productivity of the building and its occupants. This should be considered as the fundamental driving force behind the evolution of the "High Tech", "Intelligent", "Smart", "Technically Enhanced", (call it what you may) building.

Two of the most important components of the High Tech building are:

> **Integrated Systems** — Where the various parts of the electronic infrastructure – automated building services, data and communications – are bought together to the most economic level of integration which will meet the long term needs of the building.

> **Integrated Services** – Where one or more organisations come together to design, supply, install, finance and operate systems within a building.

This paper studies how these two aspects of the High Tech building are evolving and what the implications will be to the building industry.

## THE INEVITABLE SHIFT IN THE BUILDING INDUSTRY

We have seen over the last ten years a major shift in the pattern of expenditure in the construction of buildings. Figure 1 shows how the proportion of total construction costs of new and refurbished buildings in the USA and Western Europe accounted for by the shell has declined substantially over these years. In contrast the mechanical and electrical services and scenary as a proportion of the total is increasing.

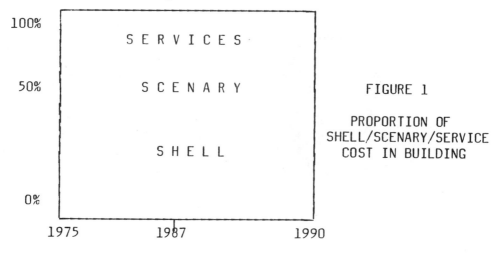

FIGURE 1

PROPORTION OF SHELL/SCENARY/SERVICE COST IN BUILDING

This proportion will depend on the type of building concerned from say 20% service cost in a speculative office development to 50% in a information technology intensive financial services office.

The major influences are:
- o Growth in service sector
- o Growth in information technology and its related support services
- o Need for increased productivity
- o Need to cater for greater flexibility in usage
- o Increased expectations in the working environment
- o Deregulation of the telecommunications industry
- o Need for "intelligence" to manage the increase in technology in the building
- o Decline in hardware costs
- o Emergance of communication standards

Initially the more forward thinking property developers are recognising this and are incorporating state-of-the-art technology to increase their chances of selling in a buyers market.

## THE TECHNOLOGY

There are a whole range of products and services involved in an Intelligent Building all at different stages of development, different life cycles, and at various levels of acceptance. Intelligent buildings are an evolution and there is no clear cut-off where traditional buildings end and intelligent buildings start.

The evolution of systems within a building is coming from three main areas:

**°Building Management Systems** including
- Environmental Control System
- Energy Management Systems
- Fire alarm/life support systems
- Security systems, card access and closed circuit television
- Lift management system
- Maintenance management systems
- Maximum demand systems
- And others

**°Telecommunication Systems** (Voice & Data) including:
- Telephones
- Workstations with word processing, filing, diaries, computing, spread sheets, message pads and other facilities
- Document transfer and electronic mail
- Mainframe computers

- Teleconferencing
- Telex
- Facsimile
- Public and Private Data Bases
- Private Branch Exchanges (PBX)

° Cable Management & Future Proofing
  - Power cables
  - Telecommunication cables
  - Data cables
  - Control cables
  - Local and wide area networks (LAN,WAN)
  - Cordless technology
  - Cable routing and data base systems

Along with this increase of technology comes a need to design the fabric and structure to incorporate and manage it. Early consideration in the design of the building must include:

o Flexible HVAC control
o Location of office/building automation equipment
o Switch and communication closets
o Column spacing
o Floor, wall and ceiling design to incorporate greater quantities of cable possible for more flexible interconnections
o Riser capacity, location and access
o Etc

## EVOLUTION TOWARDS INTEGRATION

We are seeing a gradual integration to what one could call a **"systems solution"** to this technology.

In the area of Building management systems there has been a trend towards the integration of these systems to form **Integrated Building Management Systems (IBMS).** Many of the larger controls companies are offering various levels of true or perceived integration. The method of integration is by use of common "intelligent" outstations (data gathering panels or field interface units), common data highways and centralisation of all services at one location. This approach not only provides greater economies in installation but also provides the user with more flexibility. More and more consultants are now specifiying the IBMS approach both here in the UK and elsewhere in Europe.

Similarly on the telecommunications side both voice and data are coming together through the use of digital PBXs. These exchanges and their related telephones are still expensive and the number of data channels are limited. The next major step forward will be the introduction of **INTEGRATED SERVICES DIGITAL NETWORKS** (ISDN). This will provide the integration of voice and data over both private and public networks. Although a few leading telecommunication suppliers are already offering such systems using defacto standards, most are awaiting a commonly agreed international standard expected in 1988.

There is now much talk about integrating the IBMS and ISDN but other than using the PBX for multiplexing, this is unlikely to happen for a number of years if at all. Many people think that they would be putting "too many eggs in one basket". The most likely approach will be some form of gateway between systems.

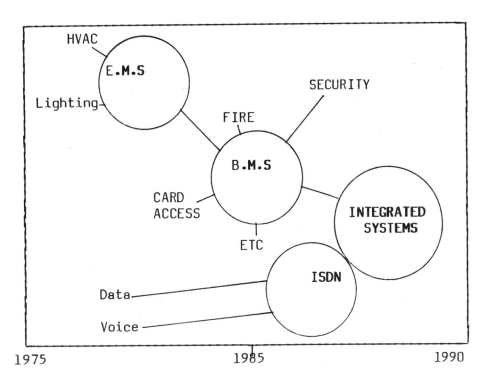

FIGURE 2 - EVOLUTION OF BUILDING SERVICES & TELECOM SYSTEM
INTEGRATION

Trends in cable management especially in the field of film optics are integrating the mass of copper cables, traditionally found in buildings, into a few fibre cables. This will become most evident on the financial trading floors of the city.

Integration of design, installation and management of this technology is also emerging and nowhere is this more evident than in the U.S.A.

## DEVELOPMENTS IN THE U.S.A.

Intelligent buildings are an evolution in the building industry not a definable structure. Therefore the number of such buildings and their degree of integration cannot be defined.

The vast majority of intelligent buildings are in the U.S.A. These are mostly (probably 80%) commercial office blocks usually with **shared tennant services** (STS) almost to the point where intelligent buildings are synonymous with STS buildings.

The market for intelligent buildings, integrated systems and services has been very much technology and vendor driven by computer, telecommunication and building controls companies - leader in the field being Honeywell. It has been very much a "missionary" sell where eventually they will hope these systems and services will become as common as air conditioning.

It has also been a god send to the U.S.property developer who with a high level of vacancies (typical 15-20% in some main commercial centres) has needed to enhance his property and provide a more state-of-the-art image. It has been shown that where two or more properties in the same location meet a prospective tenant/buyers main cirteria (such as location, image, space available length of lease, cost etc) that the more "intelligent" building can tip the balance. Furthermore where the building is sufficiently future proofed the tenant will often accept a longer lease.

The majority of successful Intelligent Building developments in the U.S.A seem to have a number of things in common including:

(1) The specification for the systems and related services are drawn up at the conceptual stage of the building by a project team led by the architect or developer and includes the representatives of the most likely system suppliers, the building owner or operator and the "anchor" tenant if already identified. This is a major change for the suppliers (building controls + telecommunications) who were not usually involved until later in the project and at a much later stage in the decision tree.

(2) The developers prefer those suppliers of systems and technology who can provide "one stop shopping" to ensure proper integration of products and systems.

(3) The management (operation and maintenance) of the systems were carried out by a business entity set up either by the developer, the supplier or a joint venture between both. The joint venture approach seems the most preferable. The quality of this service is felt to be the major factor of overall success.

In most instances the integrated services management organisation (referred to in (3) above), finances the system and then charges a management fee to cover the capital cost and day to day operation. This has proved to be an additional source of revenue for the developer where he has become involed in the management.

## THE TREND

Inevitably like any market, these "inovative" developers have taken the initiative, they are small in number and they are probably reaching their peak in High Tech building investment. "Imitators" will wait to see the result of these early installations which will probably not start coming through until the late '80s and early '90s when leases will reach renewal dates. In the mean time suppliers will consolidate and the smaller less successful companies will be squeezed out as competition steps up and margins are squeezed.

Factors which will dictate the transition period from "inovators" to "imitators" and dictate the rules of future growth are:

o How well the benefits and cost effectiveness can be demonstrated

o The speed general building codes and fire/safety standards can keep up with the intelligent building technology

o System protocols, compatability and standards which provide clients with flexibility and long term security

o How quickly the market can be educated and change their buying habits

o The reliability of systems and quality of support

## IMPLICATION TO THE EUROPEAN MARKET

Features that inhibit the integrated approach and systems solutions to High Tech buildings this side of the Atlantic include:

- ° Developers, agents and investors
  - conservative approach to construction
  - dominance of "net lettable space criteria" at the expense of service provision
  - lack of awareness of technology

- ° Occupants and Tenants
  - reluctance of capital investment to save running cost
  - seperation of responsibility between building services and communication services

- ° Suppliers
  - highly fragmented industry with no true "one stop shopping"
  - reluctance to co-operate on standards
  - poor reputations of some HVAC & BMS installations

Already we are seeing groups of companies coming together in the U.K. to set up "one-stop-shopping". This is particularly evident between the building management and fire and security system suppliers. However, we see little evidence yet of the system solution in the U.K, where a company can offer the High Tech products and systems - building management, telecommunications and cable management - as well as carry out the overall design, turn key project management and installation, finance the installation and then manage it. Not until we see this type of capability will the intelligent building take roots in the U.K.

# High-tech buildings: the pipeline & players

PHIL GUSACK
DIRECTOR, OFFICES AND PROPERTY DEVELOPMENT
FITCH & COMPANY DESIGN CONSULTANTS PLC
LONDON, ENGLAND

1    THE PIPELINE AND PLAYERS
     What is being planned, what is being built and who
     is doing most of it?

2    SPACE INVADERS
     Big Bang & Little Bangs - the consolidators, the
     relocators and the victims.

3    OFFICE DESIGN - FACT & FICTION
     What do people do in office buildings anyway?

4    WHAT ABOUT THE WORKERS?
     Work versus lifestyle.

5    THINKING THE UNTHINKABLE
     What happens when corporate planning is only good for
     three years but rent reviews last for five?

Phil Gusack has worked on a
wide variety of high-tech
planning and design projects
in the United States and
Britain - hospitals, laboratories, offices, electronics
factories and bank head-
quarters. He now runs the
Office and Property Development Division at Fitch & Co.

Presented at HIGH-TECH BUILDINGS 87: Online Publications, Pinner, UK, 1987

THE PIPELINE AND PLAYERS

1    Notwithstanding the Golden Triangle, the M25, Telford
     Swindon or Milton Keynes, the real centre of high-
     tech building today is London.

2    Of an estimated UK total of 600 million sq ft of
     office stock, (DoE), 200 million sq ft is in Greater
     London and three-quarters of that is in Central
     London.

3    However, by value, we estimate 65% is concentrated in
     Central London.  The rest of London represents a
     further 5-10% and the rest of the UK only about 25%.

4    Within five miles of this venue, construction is
     proceeding on over 200 projects which we roughly
     estimate at £800 million in construction value,
     (exclusive of tenant fitting-out costs!).

5    In today's post-industrial economy, every large
     office building is bound to accommodate and utilize
     high-tech systems of one kind or another.  Our
     analysis of projects of 50,000 gsf or more,
     identifies the following:

|  | TOTAL | NEW BUILD | AVAILABLE NEW BUILD | | |
|---|---|---|---|---|---|
| Under Construction | 73 | 54 | 31 | ie | 42% |
| With Planning Consent | 104 | 91 | 77 | ie | 74% |
| Planning Applications | 70 | 60 | 57 | ie | 81% |

6    We have identified 14 pre-let projects, each of
     50,000 gsf or more of new construction; these total
     1.4 million gsf.

7    Our league tables identify the top ten developers,
     architects and contractors in volume terms.  In the
     last three years over 800 developers and 350 arch-
     itects have played a part.

8    Focusing only on major projects, ie high-tech
     buildings, (100,000 gsf or more).  The estimated
     demand in 1986 was three million sq ft, (source;
     Jones Lang Wootton).  We identify probable comple-
     tions in excess of 27 million sq ft by 1990.


                    SPACE INVADERS


1    Central London dominates the UK office market
     simply because of the concentration of quality occ-
     upiers and their high-performance facility require-
     ments.

2    Although Big Bang itself obviously created unprec-
     edented demand for high-tech facilities - banking
     factories, etc, most UK-based integrated securities
     houses still operate from more than one building,
     (eg Morgan Grenfell, SG Warburg, Kleinwort,
     Citicorp etc, etc), despite major property acquisi-
     tions.

3    Foreign banks employ over 54,000 staff in Central
     London but only about 2,500 elsewhere in teh UK.

4    However, the representation by country of origin
     interests  us the most.  The Japanese dominate the
     banking league tables, but still employ compara-
     tively few staff here.  Can this continue for much
     longer?

5    London is also the centre of the legal profession.
     Here growth and mergers have been dramatic.  There
     are now 27 law firms who employ 200 or more staff.
     The top eight jointly employ over 5,000.  We have
     identified 27 firms with 50 or more staff who will
     soon move premises.

6    Advertising is another "little bang".  The top 45
     conglomerates and firms are in London.  We have
     identified 16 that employ more than 200 staff.

7    In mid-March the legal profession was actually a
     bigger market force than Japanese banks! but for
     how long?


             OFFICE DESIGN : FACT AND FICTION


1    It would be convenient to imagine that we have,
     collectively made a conceptual breakthrough.  Now
     that '60s building leases have expired, the buildings
     themselves have been deemed technically obsolete.
     Today's players are confident they will not make
     the same mistakes again.

2    No office building fit for the '90s is now complete
     without air-conditioning, raised floors and an
     atrium.  The name of the game is wire management
     and the goal is to get micros on every desk without
     showing the wires.

3    Insofar as it goes, all this is fine.  But there's
     more to it than comfort, control and glare-free
     lighting.  Technical design criteria alone define an
     unreal world - one in which the high point of
     design is the creation of perfect conditions for
     moving a mouse.

4    Despite the new-found technical capacity of designs
     in the pipeline, they are still firmly rooted in
     the past because they are conceived simply as multi-
     storey platforms for standardised offices and work-
     stations and not much else.

5    Is this all that tomorrow's tenants want?  Can we
     safely assume that, for the next 25 years, all will
     be well so long as we can snake enough wiring to
     each desk?

6    Companies move in and out of office buildings for
     all sorts of reasons, and technology is not
     necessarily the driving force.

## WHAT ABOUT THE WORKERS

1   The development pipeline is dominated by an unprec-
    edented number of very large projects, yet most of
    them are basically stand-alone office blocks with
    minimal retail and recreational facilities, if any.

2   Canary Wharf is unique for several obvious reasons
    - size, quality and bravura.  However, it's the only
    serious attempt to provide useful and convenient
    retailing for the office population.

3   High-tech specifications and systems in isolation
    do nothing to create a supportive working lifestyle.
    Can we afford to ignore this?

## THINKING THE UNTHINKABLE

1   Our statistics indicate that at some point in 1989,
    the current development boom could well produce
    significant over-supply.  Will developers proceed
    if they see over-supply on the horizon?  Many pro-
    jects in the pipeline for 1988 involve demolition
    of existing occupied buildings.  To get vacant
    possession means action now.

2   Those players who achieve vacant possession of dev-
    elopment sites in 1988 may well face problems.
    After all, in their efforts to catch soaring rents,
    developers have paid record prices for their sites.
    Can they simply stop at this point?

3   Take-up of space in Central London in the first
    half of the 1980's has reached 10 million sq ft a
    year, but if demand returns to pre-Big Bang levels,
    the consequences are dire.  In order to succeed,
    property development has to dregulate.  Higher
    vacancy rates will bring rents down.  The upward-
    only rent review and the 25-year FRI lease is,
    therefore, an anachronism.

4    In this environment, the customer is king and the customer -
     tenants - want buildings which help them get on with their
     business.  To remain flexible it means they want a wide range of
     choices available in the market so that they are not hamstrung
     by conventional leases.  They do want flexibility within the
     building they occupy and high-tech systems are, of course,
     central to this, but experience shows that they also want to
     work in supportive environments which reinforce their corporate
     culture and business strategies.  Competitive buildings do all
     of these things.

5    There are non-competitive buildings all over the place - Croydon
     is an obvious example.  Thinking the unthinkable means accepting
     Croydonism deep in the heart of the City.

# Order Form

Online proceedings are known throughout the world as a major source of technical and commercial information on a wide variety of high technology areas. All the proceedings are published to coincide with the conferences on which they report. Consequently Online proceedings provide topical and highly valuable insights into the state-of-the-art and future directions of todays technology.

A selection of recent Online titles is given below. These, or a catalogue, may be obtained using the form provided.

|  | US$ |
|---|---|
| [] Electronic Message Systems (86) | 160 |
| [] Electronic Publishing 86 | 150 |
| [] High-Tech Buildings 86 | 120 |
| [] Intelligent Buildings 86 | 120 |
| [] ISDN Volume 1: Europe (86) | 190 |
| [] ISDN Volume 2: USA (86) | 190 |
| [] Networks 86 | 190 |
| [] International Open Systems 87 | 190 |
| [] Satellite Communications & Broadcasting (86) | 150 |
| [] System Security (86) | 130 |

Name _____ Initials _____ Dr/Mr/Ms

Position _____

Organisation _____

Address _____

City _____ State _____ Postcode/Zip _____ Country _____

Telephone/Telex _____ Signature _____ Date _____

[] Cheque enclosed, value _____      [] Please send me a catalogue

**Despatch** To ensure Online proceedings reach you as rapidly as possible after receiving your order, all proceedings are despatched by air outside the UK. All prices quoted include despatch costs for prepaid orders.

**Return to**
Online Publications
Pinner Green House
Ash Hill Drive
Pinner, Middlesex HA5 2AE, UK

Online Publications
540 Barnum Avenue
Bridgeport, CT 06608, USA
(NB: NY & CT residents please add appropriate sales tax)

Prices correct for April 1987.